Haynes

Mobile
Technology
Manual

Published by: Haynes Publishing
Sparkford, Yeovil, Somerset BA22 7JJ, UK
Tel: 01963 442030 Fax: 01963 440001
Int. tel: +44 1963 442030 Fax: +44 1963 440001
E-mail: sales@haynes.co.uk
Website: www.haynes.co.uk

British Library Cataloguing in Publication Data:
A catalogue record for this book is available from the British Library

ISBN 1 84425 226 4

Printed in Britain by J. H. Haynes & Co. Ltd., Sparkford

Haynes

Mobile
Technology
Manual

Kyle MacRae

Contents

Introduction

This book explores the kind of tools that you might want to take with you when you travel, whether on a business trip overseas, on holiday, or simply when commuting between home and the office. After all, keeping in touch at all times in a digital age *should* be straightforward. We *should* be able to work from pretty much anywhere, home or abroad, with pretty much no disruption to normal service. But is it the reality?

No, frankly, it is not. The truth is that mobile technology is confusing, complicated and disjointed. A wander around a high-tech shop is usually sufficient to have even a technophile scurrying for cover. Laptop or PDA? Wi-Fi or Bluetooth? GSM, GPRS or 3G? And would you like GPS with that?

A functional focus

Well, we're here to help. There are two main strands in this book. First, we explore the full range of today's mobile technologies and explain what they mean. But we must stress at the outset that we steer away from the nuts and bolts, and concentrate instead on use. In other words, we don't particularly care how, say, a GPRS or 3G network works but we do care what it can do for you in practical terms.

The second strand is a critical examination of the current state of mobile hardware or gadgets. Here again we take a pragmatic approach with little emphasis on numbers and a lot on practical applications.

With new devices being released every day into an already crowded market and with publication schedules being what they are, it's clearly impossible for us to keep up to speed with the

You may have a surfeit of perplexing technologies to contend with but think yourself lucky: at least you no longer have to cart around this 15kg workhorse if you want to work away from home.

Laptops are becoming smaller, sleeker and lighter yet more powerful every day.

Part mobile phone, part handheld computer, part portable email machine. Could this be the only device you'll ever need?

very latest developments or to make specific recommendations. Many of the products you see on these pages will be superseded by fresher models within months and some by the end of this paragraph. However, it doesn't really matter. If you understand what the raw technical specs mean *and* what they can do for you, then choosing a mobile device – any mobile device – becomes much simpler.

For instance, if you understand that GPRS means an always-on internet connection on a mobile phone and appreciate that an always-on internet connection means that you can send and receive email while on the move, then you're better placed to decide whether you need a GPRS-enabled mobile phone. You can then factor in whether you also want it to function as a handheld computer, a satellite receiver, a music and video player or whatever else takes your fancy.

Small world, big picture

We look first at the four main players in the field of mobile computing: PDAs, laptop computers, so-called smartphones and Tablet PCs. We move on to explore wireless networks, with particular reference to mobile email and internet access, and look in detail at how you would use a PDA from day to day. We then expand the field by considering the emerging technologies of internet telephony and satellite navigation, and round off with a nod towards mobile entertainment (even a jetsetter needs to chill occasionally).

So that's our goal: to help you get to grips with mobile technology in the real world and, ultimately, to make an informed decision. You will, we trust, emerge with a slightly jaundiced view of 'convergence' – the tendency towards cramming as many functions as possible into a single device – and a considerably clearer understanding of both the benefits and the limitations of mobile technology.

Lighter and cheaper than a laptop but plenty powerful enough to keep you up to speed while working away from base. We'll consider PDAs in some detail throughout this book.

PART  # A buyer's guide to PDAs

PART

What is a PDA?

Computers small enough to carry in your pocket and use in the palm of your hand are sold under a variety of guises: as palmtops, PDAs, handhelds, Pocket PCs and Palm PCs.

While these labels carry very specific meanings to the initiated, to everybody else they sound like different names for the same thing. To avoid confusion we'll call them all Personal Digital Assistants (PDAs), a name which tends to understate their capabilities given that the latest models can take pictures, show movies and duplicate the functions of dedicated MP3 players. In this book when we use the terms Pocket PC and Palm PC, we shall do so only to distinguish between the two major (and incompatible) families of PDA.

Though it looks just like a Pocket PC, the aerial on this Hewlett Packard iPAQ H6340 betrays the fact that it's also a mobile phone. This is an example of 'convergence', whereby clear-cut differences between different types of device tend to disappear.

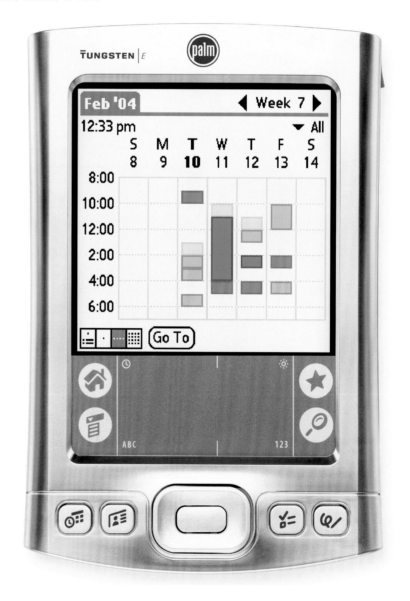

This Tungsten E from PalmOne is running one of the core applications of every PDA: time management.

The Pocket PC is equipped with a Windows-like operating system and is mainly sold by Hewlett Packard under the iPAQ brand name. A diminishing number of smaller manufacturers such as Mitac also sell Pocket PCs. Microsoft is closely connected with the design and development of Pocket PC software and hardware.

The Palm PC uses a dedicated operating system called Palm OS. Palm PCs are made mainly by a company called PalmOne. Until 2004, Sony was a major influence on the development of the Palm OS and used it in its range of CLIÉ multimedia PDAs, but these have now been discontinued in many parts of the world.

Sony's withdrawal from the scene, coupled with the fact that PalmOne has gobbled up Handspring (formerly a competitive offshoot) means that the company now has a virtual monopoly of the Palm OS market. It currently produces three ranges: Zire, Tungsten and Treo.

PDA versus laptop

Unlike a laptop computer, which attempts to duplicate most or all the facilities of a desktop PC in a smaller, portable format, a PDA provides a limited set of functions and is designed to be used *in conjunction with* a desktop PC, not as its replacement.

A PDA uses less power than a laptop, so it will run for much longer between charges; and it is very much smaller because it employs a touch-sensitive screen that makes both mouse and keyboard redundant. Instead, users control their PDAs by tapping on-screen buttons and icons with a plastic stylus and input data by using the stylus as an electronic pen to 'write' on the screen. Later, we'll look at other ways of getting data into a PDA but, when you're on the road, the stylus is the main option. If you misplace your stylus, a blunt pencil or almost any pointed-but-not-too-sharp object will do.

Early PDAs had monochrome screens – some of them downright murky – but most of today's models have bright, sharp screens capable of displaying thousands of colours. The TFT screen technology is no different from that used by laptops, flat-screen desktop monitors and digital cameras. The real difference is in size. For instance, the standard iPAQ Pocket PC screen is only 3.5-inch (89mm) compared to the 14-inch and upwards of a laptop. Clearly the screen size places a number of restrictions on the type of software that can be used, and anything involving graphic design and print layout is problematic. Spreadsheet and word processing programs work fine, but only because they are heavily modified for use on smaller screens.

Laptop and notebook computers pack an awful lot of processing power into a portable format, but this ZV5000 from Hewlett Packard is power-hungry, heavy and expensive compared to the company's PDAs. Do you really need to lug around a full-blown computer?

How do you use yours?

To function as a useful ancillary device, a PDA must 'talk' to and share data with a host PC. The idea is that you download essential data from your desktop PC onto the PDA and take it with you while away from the home or office. Of course, what counts as essential varies from person to person. For some it might be a company's current price list, whilst for others it's the latest MP3 downloads to play when they're on the road. In addition, there's a core set of functions built into every PDA, whether Pocket PC or Palm PC, including an address book, calculator, appointments diary, task list and note taking facilities. Any changes or additions made to data on the PDA are reconciled with the desktop PC when you return to base.

The lifeline between a PDA and its host PC is special synchronisation software built into the PDA and provided on CD for installation on the desktop PC. The usual means of connection between the two is high-speed USB cable, but you can also synchronise over a Bluetooth short-range radio link or a Wi-Fi wireless network. Most PDAs are sold with a cradle to which both the USB cable and a power lead are attached. Dropping the PDA into its cradle automatically conducts a 'hot synch' of data with the desktop PC and starts topping up the rechargeable battery in the PDA. When you're ready to leave, simply lift the PDA from its cradle and you're on your way.

Dropping a PDA into its cradle charges its battery and connects it to its host PC via a USB cable.

PART 1

Palm PC or Pocket PC?

Although they look superficially alike, there are big differences between Palm PCs and Pocket PCs. The primary distinction is the operating system. If you're a dyed-in-the-wool Windows fan, you'll probably prefer a Pocket PC equipped with the current pocket version of Windows. At the time of writing (early 2005), this is Windows Mobile 2003 Second Edition.

If you're a Mac owner, your best buy is a Palm PC. This comes with synchronisation software for both PCs and Macs. The facilities available to Mac users are not as sophisticated as for PC users but at least they're free and they're built into the portable device. Although it is possible to synchronise a Pocket PC with a Mac, this requires the purchase of third party software. One of the popular choices is Missing Sync from **www.markspace.com** but there are several others, most of which are available on free trial for limited periods.

If you're a PC owner, there is no reason to prefer either Pocket PC or Palm PC purely in terms of compatibility with your desktop machine. The synchronisation software for both types of PDA is equally well designed and easy to use, so your choice of PDA will depend on the exact features you need and how much you're prepared to pay.

Here's a quick comparative analysis of the two types of device.

Palm PC plus points

- Smaller and lighter than a Pocket PC and with better battery life. This is mainly due to the use of smaller display screens and less powerful processors (the Palm OS needs fewer resources than Windows).
- Better selection of third party software. This is because Palm-style PDAs have been around for longer and have a larger share of the market. As always when buying a computer, you should check the availability of the software you think you'll need before tying yourself to a particular operating system.
- Lower prices, especially if you choose one of the cheaper Palm machines which supplies only a basic set of features. When you compare top-of-the-range models equipped with equivalent features, the price gap is less significant.
- Good integration with Microsoft Office. It might seem strange but the Dataviz 'Documents to Go' program included with most Palm PCs provides better tools for working with Office documents than the Word and Excel programs built into a Pocket PC.
- A more stable operating system that doesn't slow down when the memory fills up, as happens with a heavily-used Pocket PC.

Pocket PC plus points

- Bigger screens and higher resolutions allow you to see more on a single screen without having to scroll.
- Twice as many input techniques (four instead of two), including handwriting recognition.
- Strong support in certain specialist areas such as GPS and route finding.
- Pocket Internet Explorer is built into the operating system.
- More memory available for user data, without having to resort to a memory expansion card.
- Better file organisation (using folders) and easier task switching using Pocket PC's own implementation of the Windows Taskbar and Start menu.

A PDA from either stable is undeniably a useful accessory in a busy life. We'll try to help you decide whether it's truly essential.

Before you make up your mind ...

When you compare a Palm PC such as the Zire 72 with a Pocket PC such as the HP iPAQ 3700, they seem to have much in common: four-way controllers, bright colour screens, built-in cameras, voice recorders, built-in Bluetooth radio communication, and SDIO expansion slots that can be used for memory cards or plug-in accessories. So why should the iPAQ cost at least half as much again as the Zire? The answer is that it offers more: not only in the form of a convenient desktop synchronise cradle but also by providing Wi-Fi wireless networking and Bluetooth radio. The rest of the price difference can be accounted for by the fact that it is fitted with more memory and has a faster, more expensive processor.

Palm PCs don't carry the huge burden of having to run Windows so, despite being superficially less powerful than Pocket PCs, users generally find it impossible to say whether one is faster than the other. If you're happy to do without a cradle and don't need Wi-Fi, the Zire seems the better buy. Then again, the Zire's screen is smaller than that of the iPAQ 3700 so it's less suitable for watching movies.

What should be clear is that choosing between a Palm PC and a Pocket PC isn't a heart-and-soul cultural decision like choosing between a PC and a Mac. Rather, it's a practical buying exercise. We recommend comparing the specifications of individual machines, regardless of their operating system, and then buying what comes closest to meeting your current and anticipated future needs. At the same time you should compare the software included with each machine to see which best suits your needs.

The next section will help you decide what to look for.

An iPAQ can function as a universal remote control. Now if that's not a killer selling point for a device costing several hundred pounds, we don't know what is!

PART ① PDAs: inside and out

Even if you know your way around the inside of a desktop PC, it won't help you much when you want to evaluate the features of a PDA. For a start, there's no hard disk (all the data and programs are stored in memory). Neither is the speed of the processor an over-riding factor as it is with a desktop or laptop machine. There are no CD or DVD drives and you have to start thinking of memory in terms of kilobytes and megabytes instead of gigabytes.

PDA manufacturers don't assemble their machines with the mix-and-match abandon of desktop PC manufacturers. There's no question of being able to swap a PDA's processor to gain extra speed or of having a larger screen fitted. The tightly integrated construction of a PDA means you have to turn the whole PC buying process on its head. Instead of making a wish list of features and then checking suppliers to see who can provide them at the lowest possible price, it's easier to look at which PDAs are currently on offer and then to choose the one that comes closest to your ideal and falls within your budget. If you stick to the two main manufacturers, HP and PalmOne, you'll have around 20 PDAs to choose from: nothing like the thousands of permutations of make and model facing buyers of a desktop PC.

At the end of this section there's a run-down of the models available from HP and PalmOne in early 2005, along with website details where you can discover what's on offer at the present time.

Getting to know your PDA

Every PDA is different but they all have a lot of features in common. The iPAQ rx3715, illustrated here, is one of HP's Mobile Multimedia devices. It therefore has more buttons and controls than a standard PDA. Here's what they all do:

LED indicates charging status and also acts as warning light for certain events.

LED indicates that Bluetooth and Wi-Fi are turned on.

Shutter release for digital camera; also acts as start button for voice recorder when pressed for longer period.

Programmable control button, initially set to turn on the device's ability to act as a universal remote controller for domestic devices.

Programmable control button, initially set to summon HP Image Zone, in order to view, edit or print digital images.

Programmable control button, initially set to operate as the iTask trigger, which gives access to the applications and settings screens.

Programmable control button, initially set to launch Mobile Media, for viewing pictures and videos or listening to music.

4-way scrolling plus a central command button are incorporated in the integrated navigation device.

Expansion slot for SD and MMC memory cards, and for SDIO add-on devices. Remove the plastic blanking plate, as shown here, before inserting an SD card.

Power button. Press and hold to turn device on or off.

Stylus input device for touch sensitive screen. Pull to remove.

3.5mm jack socket for standard stereo headphones.

Small parabolic mirror allows you to see a reflection of yourself when composing a self portrait.

Camera lens for 1.2 megapixel camera. It has no protective cap.

Recessed reset button restarts the rx3715 without losing any stored data if, for any reason, the device fails to respond to commands.

Universal connector carries both USB signals and AC current. Also fits into cradle adapter.

Understanding the specs

To compare PDAs, you've got to know a little bit about how they work and what each component is for. A desktop PC with only 32MB of memory would be virtually unusable but 32MB is actually quite respectable for a PDA. Be prepared to cast aside any preconceptions based on a knowledge of desktop PCs.

Memory

There are two types of memory in every PDA: Flash ROM (Read Only Memory) and RAM (Random Access Memory). The Flash ROM contains the operating system and pre-installed programs. RAM is where the pre-installed programs run and where you store your own data.

The amount of Flash ROM is determined by the manufacturer and, in normal circumstances, can't be changed by the user. Far more significant to the user is the amount of RAM, because this is where programs are operated and personal data is stored: 16MB to 64MB is typical.

As a rule of thumb, a Pocket PC needs twice as much RAM as a Palm PC because of the heavy demands made by Windows. Palm PCs are much more frugal with memory. But whichever type of PDA you choose, always bear in mind that if you want to carry massive amounts of data around with you – perhaps so you can use your PDA as a mobile photo album, MP3 player or pocket theatre – you'll need additional memory in the form of a slot-in memory expansion card.

Some HP iPAQ Pocket PCs offer what seems to be a new type of memory called File Store. It is used to store backup copies of important data and programs. File Store memory is actually an extension of the Flash ROM that contains Windows and the built-in software. It can only be accessed by a special iPAQ backup program, so you can't use it for running programs or storing 'live' data.

While it's great to have this portable backup facility, you still need to back up your iPAQ's contents to the hard disk of your PC in case you ever lose your PDA. When comparing specs, be sure to take account of File Store memory. HP advertises its hx4700 model as having up to 135MB of 'user available memory' but, because 80MB of this is File Store, only 55MB can be used for programs and data.

File Store memory appears in System Settings on the Storage tab and not as part of the main memory.

Pocket PC users can fine tune how the available memory is apportioned between running programs and storing data.

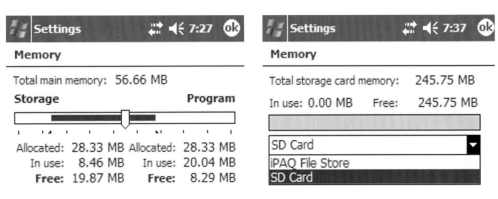

This is HP's battery universal charger, pictured with an extended-life replacement battery for the iPAQ hx4700.

Batteries and power consumption

Most PDAs are powered by flat Lithium-Ion batteries, rather like the ones used in mobile phones. In the case of certain Pocket PCs, these can be removed easily and replaced. A small internal backup battery retains the data in main memory long enough for you to fit the replacement. Unless you are willing to pay big bucks for a special battery charger, keeping several batteries topped up will mean sticking to a careful regime of battery rotation in your PDA to make sure the spares are always fully charged. However, you don't have to worry about losing data if a

PDA battery loses its charge and no spare is available, because even when there is insufficient power to start the device enough remains to maintain the memory for at least a week. This gives you ample time to recharge the battery.

If you choose a PDA with sealed internal batteries, they can still be replaced when they lose their capacity to hold a full charge, but as this means dismantling the case it's probably something you'd want to leave to a dealer.

Some devices with colour screens are hard-pressed to run for six hours, even with screens dimmed and wireless facilities disabled. If you constantly use wireless communication, watch movies or listen to MP3 music while using your PDA, you could see battery life drop to three hours or less. While three hours is ample if you use your PDA intermittently throughout the day, it may not be enough for a long flight or train journey. The batteries in Palm PCs tend to soldier on for longer than those in Pocket PCs, but this is mainly because their screens are smaller and they use less powerful processors.

Manufacturers can be very vague about battery life and when figures are quoted they are likely to be on the optimistic side. If extended battery life is important to you, then you'll need to do some research by reading magazine and web reviews. Even better, if you're buying a machine that's already been on sale for a while, check out any online forums or user groups devoted to the machine. You're bound to find that battery life is a hot topic and the opinions of owners whose experience is of using their PDAs in real-world situations is more valuable than a reviewer's one-off battery test.

If you'd rather take a technical approach, examine the published specs for the machines you're thinking of buying and compare their capacities. Battery capacity is expressed in terms of milliamps per hour (mAh). 900–1800mAh is common for Pocket PCs but higher capacity (i.e. more durable) batteries of up to 3600mAh can be purchased as optional accessories.

Under the covers, you'll find a rechargeable Lithium-Ion battery.

Screens

When expressed as a number of vertical and horizontal pixels, the resolution of a screen tells you how many dots are used to make up the picture. A resolution of 320 x 240 is typical. The number of colours is even more important, especially for photographs and videos. Look for a screen capable of displaying 65,536 colours, a figure which is sometimes expressed as 64K and at other times as 65K. Don't worry about the discrepancy, which is just the result of different ways of counting. HP tends to be rather coy about the resolution of its screens and prefers to talk about 3.5in and 4in screens, so you may have to dig deep if you want to make accurate comparisons.

Although both Pocket PCs and Palm PCs appear to have rectangular screens of roughly identical dimensions, this is not the case. On a Palm PC, more than a quarter of what appears to be the screen is actually the user input area. This area is not capable of displaying anything because it is pre-printed with control icons and contains a blank central panel where you can write with the stylus.

Most Palm PCs (the Tungsten T3 and Zire 72 are exceptions) have square screens capable of displaying 160 x 160 pixels. The Zire 72 and other prestige models have high resolution screens capable of displaying 320 x 320 pixels. Bear in mind that the dots on a Zire 72 are crammed into a smaller area than on a Pocket PC so 320 x 320 represents a very sharp picture indeed, especially as it displays 65,536 colours.

Figures don't tell you everything: some screens are brighter and sharper than others with similar dimensions and specifications; and some screens can cope very well with direct sunlight while others become almost unusable. If possible, try to get a hands-on demonstration of any device you're thinking of buying, both indoors and outdoors, before making a decision.

The 640 x 480 pixel screen of the HP iPAQ hx4700 is the highest resolution of any PDA.

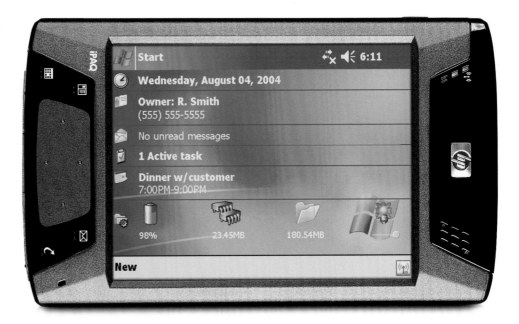

This plug-in card adds Bluetooth capabilities to any Pocket PC with an SDIO expansion slot.

Communications features

Early PDAs had two means of communication with other devices: a USB link for connection to a host computer and an infrared beam to share data with laptops and other PDAs. Many current PDAs are additionally equipped with one or more forms of wireless communication: Wi-Fi for connection to private and public wireless networks and Bluetooth for one-to-one exchanges with external devices such as mobile phones, modems and other PDAs.

Whether you need wireless communication depends on how you intend using your PDA. If you have a need or yearning to browse the web and receive email throughout the day, wherever you are, Bluetooth is an easy way of connecting your PDA to the modem in your mobile phone. Wi-Fi is useful if you wish to share data between your PDA and a home or office network, or use public hotspots to connect to the internet.

If you don't need wireless communication, don't pay for it. You can always add Bluetooth or Wi-Fi capabilities at a later date by means of an expansion card.

Expansion slots

Nearly all current PDAs have at least one SDIO slot, and sometimes two, while others may also sport a CompactFlash slot. SDIO slots accept SD (Secure Digital) memory modules and a wide range of input and output devices including Bluetooth and Wi-Fi transmitters, modems and GPS receivers.

If you plan to use your PDA as an MP3 player or for any kind of extensive media storage, a memory card is essential. This means that if you might also want to add upgrades such as wireless networking, you should buy a PDA with two slots *or* with the necessary communications facilities built into it.

Other features

Most Pocket PCs and Palm PCs are equipped with four separate control buttons on the front, plus some form of directional controller. The control buttons are pre-programmed for specific functions – typically Calendar, Contacts, Tasks and Notepad on a Palm PC – but they can be reassigned to different functions by the user.

On most devices the directional controller is a four-way pad with a central button that can be used to confirm actions. Cheaper machines may feature only a two-way controller that scrolls the screen up or down. While a four-way controller is sometimes more convenient, especially when using the machine one-handed, it is by no means essential and every PDA program is designed to work just as well without one.

Not every PDA has an earphone socket, but any device that can play media files will have one. Check whether earphones are included. In many cases they are not. Also check whether there's a voice memo function. This allows you to record messages and reminders for yourself on occasions when it's inconvenient to use the screen and may also enable you to record dictation which can later be turned into text using speech recognition software running on the host PC. If a voice memo feature is important to

Some of the more ambitious PDA games, as well as serious software, are supplied on SD expansion cards.

It's not just mobile phones that come with built-in cameras these days. Indeed, many PDAs function as both cameras and phones, as well as much else besides.

you, look for a device with a built-in microphone and a dedicated voice memo button that enables you to record without having to use the screen and go through the usual menu system. It can be convenient to review voice memos after recording them so make sure that the built-in speaker is loud enough and clear enough for you to hear. Ask for a demonstration in the shop.

Both PalmOne and HP now sell PDAs with built-in digital cameras, capable of taking still and moving images. While the resolution and picture quality is nowhere near as good as from a dedicated camera, it's a fun item and a convenience feature you might think it's worth paying extra for, especially if you don't already own a digital camera or camera-equipped phone.

Another useful extra is a carrying case which, rather surprisingly, is not always provided. Some iPAQs, such as the hx4700, are equipped with transparent covers that fold over to shield the screen from scratches, but these do not offer any protection against dropping the entire unit onto a hard surface.

This Zire 31 has its square screen clearly visible. The bottom third of the display is the user input area.

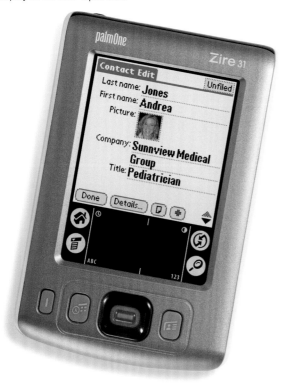

The Tungsten T3 is unusual in having a large rectangular display instead of the usual square Palm screen. It is here seen in MP3 player mode with supplied earphones.

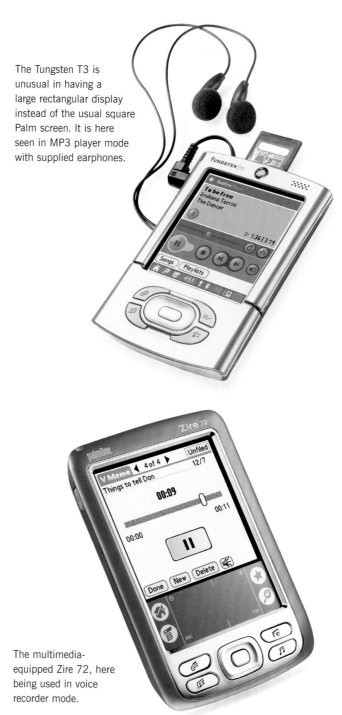

Palm PCs on the web

For an up-to-date overview of current Palm PCs visit **www.palmone.com/us** and follow the link to 'Products'. Palm also has regionalised sites for most parts of the world. What follows is a quick run-down of the hardware that's on offer in early 2005.

PalmOne PDAs are organised into three families called Treo, Tungsten and Zire. The Treo family are smartphones (see p.40), some with built-in cameras and QWERTY keyboards. The Tungsten range contains mid-to-high-end devices, most of which are equipped with fast processors, plenty of memory, Bluetooth and Wi-Fi communication facilities and excellent build quality, for high-powered business users. They're not actually made of Tungsten but they look as if they are!

The Zire range is aimed at consumers who pay for their own machines instead of having them supplied by an employer. It was developed as a low-cost alternative to the Tungsten range, enabling buyers to pay for only the features they need. There are three models to choose from: 21, 31 and 72. The Zire 21 is an entry-level machine providing the basic 'organiser' functions. It has 8MB of memory and no backlight for the monochrome screen. The Zire 31 has a colour screen 160 pixels square, a four-way navigation controller and a headphone jack for listening to MP3 files. The trendy Zire 72 is Palm's multimedia breakthrough machine, with 32MB of memory, a screen resolution of 320 x 320 pixels, a built-in voice recorder and a 1.2 megapixel camera. It is the only Zire model to feature Bluetooth connectivity for email, web browsing and wireless synchronisation with a PC. To keep prices as low as possible, none of the Zire models comes with a charging cradle.

The multimedia-equipped Zire 72, here being used in voice recorder mode.

The entry-level cradle-free Zire 21 with monochrome screen.

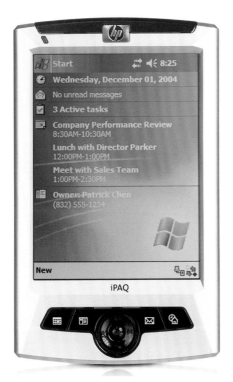

The iPAQ rz1710 is a no-frills
machine from Hewlett Packard.

The hx4700 is the power-user's
iPAQ, with a VGA screen, plenty
of memory, built-in Bluetooth and
Wi-Fi, plus twin expansion slots.

The iPAQ hx2700 is a mid-range
device, here seen sporting its
protective flip cover for the screen.

HP Pocket PCs on the web

You'll find a round-up of iPAQ Pocket PCs at **www.hp.com**. Not
all of them are available world-wide, so choose your country from
the drop-down list and then select 'Handheld Devices'.

The cheapest model is the rz1710 with a colour screen, 25MB
of memory, a 200MHz processor and no wireless communication
facilities apart from an infrared port. In the hx2000 range there
are three models with processors up to 624MHz, as much as
185MB of user memory and a range of communication options.
Every model has a screen capable of displaying 65,536 colours,
a replaceable battery and either CompactFlash or SDIO type
expansion slots.

The rx3715 is hailed as a Mobile Media Companion. As well
as a 400MHz processor and lots of user memory, it boasts
Bluetooth and Wi-Fi networking, a screen which you can turn on
its side and use in landscape mode to watch movies, a built-in
1.3 megapixel camera, an SDIO expansion slot and the ability to
function as a universal remote control for virtually any kind of
domestic device.

Top of the standard iPAQ range is the hx4700, which boasts a
4in colour screen of 640 x 480 pixels (this is the original VGA
standard that was used for many years on 14-inch desktop
monitors). Another claim to fame is a unique touch-sensitive
control pad positioned beneath the screen. This works very like
the trackpad controls found on conventional laptops and is in
addition to all the standard methods of stylus input. With a fast
processor, ample memory, stereo audio output, two expansion
slots, two types of wireless communication and a virtually
indestructible magnesium body, this is an impressive machine.
The only thing it lacks is a camera, which indicates it is aimed
mainly at corporate users.

The rx3715 is the iPAQ
multimedia powerhouse with a
built-in camera.

PART  # Laptops, smartphones and beyond

PART  **A look at laptops**

When you buy a desktop PC system, there are many, many variables but they all boil down to a relatively simple equation of performance and features versus budget. With laptops, the same considerations apply but there are two extra, critical considerations: size and weight. Somewhat paradoxically, the lighter the device, the more you have to pay and the less you get for your money.

So how do you find your way through this particular maze?

Key specifications

The basics of laptop design are plain to see: the keyboard is built into the system unit, the mouse is replaced by a touch-sensitive pad (usually) and the screen is fitted to the underside of a flip-up lid. But differences in design and function are significant. You can have a 'desktop replacement' laptop that does just about anything a desktop system does except hog space. A desktop

Not so much a portable as a downright luggable, this 1987 Toshiba T1000 was one of the first laptops. Battery powered with a full-size screen and a 3.5-inch floppy drive, it weighed in at a meaty 6.4lb (2.8kg).

Thanks to AVA Photographic, Swindon, and museum-of-computing.org.uk

replacement will typically have a high-performance processor, oodles of memory, a large screen and a DVD writer. It will also weigh a tonne and break your collar bone if you carry it around.

You can have a super-light, super-slim, super-sleek notebook that's stripped to the bone features-wise for the sake of portability. An ultra-portable PC may well have no DVD or CD drive at all, which means that you have to connect an external device to watch a movie or install software. See p.167 for more on this.

Or, naturally, you can have anything in between.

Screen size

All notebook PCs have slim TFT screens, ranging in size from 12 to 17 inches and beyond. A 15-inch model running a display resolution of 1024 x 768 pixels (known as an XGA display) is the norm for a desktop replacement laptop. Higher resolution screens are increasingly common: look for SXGA (1280 x 1024 pixels) and UXGA (1600 x 1200). These all have a standard 4:3 display ratio but you can also find widescreen models (WXGA) with an aspect ratio of 16:9 or 16:10. Great for movies but pretty pointless for Windows. High resolution widescreen displays are billed as WSXGA and WUXGA.

This model's 15-inch screen is the same size as a 15-inch TFT desktop monitor or roughly equivalent to a 17-inch CRT monitor.

The Centrino badge is your guarantee that a laptop is designed for top wireless performance.

Performance

Intel processors for laptops come in four flavours: a mobile version of the Pentium 4, or P4, as seen in desktop systems; a dedicated mobile design imaginatively called Pentium M; and lower performance but cheaper Celeron versions of both. The Pentium M design is based on the theoretically inferior Pentium III chip and runs at lower speeds, but it matches or beats most P4s, uses less power and stays cooler. Intel's competitor AMD also makes laptop processors but has so far won only a small share of the market. Look for the Mobile AMD Athlon 64 range or its less powerful sibling, the Sempron.

One term you can't fail to stumble upon is 'Centrino'. This is essentially an Intel marketing ploy that allows laptop manufacturers to stick a Centrino badge on the case if its innards contain a pre-determined batch of Intel components including the processor, chipset and, importantly, a wireless networking module. These are designed to offer optimal performance with minimal power use but a non-Centrino laptop may have the same processor and memory but an alternative, equally efficient networking component. The latest version of Centrino is called Sonoma and promises greater performance in key areas like audio and video.

Double Data Rate (DDR) memory is pretty much standard in laptops now, so follow the old adage that more is better and 256MB is the minimum. Trying to gauge the absolute performance of a laptop on its specification alone is impossible, thanks to indecipherable processor numbering and an overwhelming reliance of any one part of the system on every other. Even making relative, comparative judgments is fraught. In fact, the only realistic way of determining whether model A is faster than model B is by reading reviews where the hardware is put through a series of standard benchmark tests and scored accordingly. If raw performance really matters to you – especially if you want to play games on your laptop and hence need a high-performance video chip – seek out reviews in computer magazines on the web. Here are some useful links:

● **www.whatlaptop.co.uk**
● **http://laptops.engadget.com**
● **www.tomshardware.com/mobile/index.html**
● **www.vnunet.com/products/hardware**
● **http://reviews.zdnet.co.uk**

Inputs and outputs

Even a skeletal ultra-portable notebook should have a decent selection of connections. Decide which of the following are important to you:

Modem An obvious must-have unless you intend to use a broadband internet connection either directly or over a network.

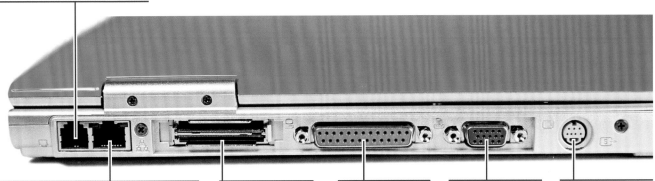

Wired networking An Ethernet port means you can hook up the notebook to any existing network via a router. These days, expect speeds of 10, 100 and 1000 Megabits per second (Mb/sec). The fastest speed is often referred to as Gigabit Ethernet.

Port replicator An interface that can be used to add a PS/2 (mouse) socket and assorted other ports via a plug-in adapter.

Parallel port An aging interface that's still occasionally useful for connecting to aging printers.

VGA A socket that lets you connect a full-size monitor.

TV-out Hook your notebook up to a TV set when playing a movie or a game.

PC Card slot An essential interface for connecting all manner of credit card-sized extra components (a wireless networking card, for instance). Most larger laptops can accommodate two Type II cards or one, thicker Type III card, while more portable models usually have room for one Type II card alone.

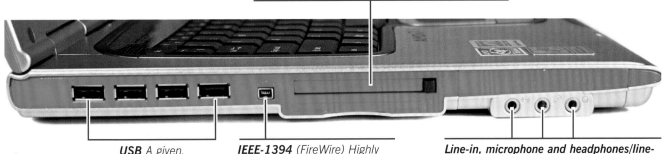

USB A given.

IEEE-1394 (FireWire) Highly desirable, particularly if you need to connect external drives or music players or capture video from a digital camcorder.

Line-in, microphone and headphones/line-out ports Listen to music or movie soundtracks on something other than the notebook's own scrawny speakers and record your own sounds.

Keyboard *Always QWERTY style, like a desktop system's keyboard, but not always full size. Some keys will have dual or triple functions and you may find special shortcut keys for, say, firing up your internet browser or email program.*

Touchpad *A motion-sensitive pad that lets you control the mouse with a finger and make left and right clicks with your thumb.*

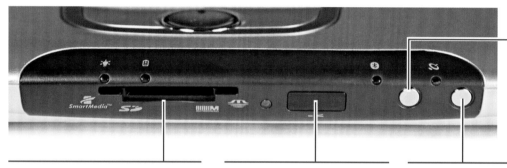

Bluetooth *'Talk' to other Bluetooth-enabled devices like printers, mobile phones and desktop systems without wires. This button turns Bluetooth on and off.*

Card reader *Some laptops come with integrated multi-format memory card readers. By popping a memory card in here, you can transfer files to and from digital cameras and PDAs without having to connect the devices directly.*

Infrared *With a mobile phone equipped with a modem, a lot of patience and a fair wind, you can connect your notebook to the internet. Increasingly uncommon.*

Wireless networking *Wi-Fi lets you network without cables. Perfect for wireless networks at home – who wants network cables trailing across the living room? – and useful for tapping into wireless hotspots around the world (see p.59). This button turns Wi-Fi on and off.*

Battery life

A serious consideration. Battery life is dependent upon several factors, including the notebook's hardware specification and how hard you work it. In an extreme case, a notebook may run flat in under an hour; at the other extreme, you may get three hours of continuous power. Again, read some reviews or benchmark tests and don't place too much faith in the manufacturers' figures. Lithium-Ion is the technology to trust.

A notebook's batteries recharge whenever you run it on mains power, so do this at every opportunity. Also consider getting a spare battery – and remember to charge it and carry it with you. There's nowt like missing the last ten minutes of a DVD movie to tip a frazzled lounge-bound traveller over the edge.

Drives

You can expect upwards of a 40GB hard drive and at least a DVD-ROM or CD-RW optical drive. On ultra-portable models, the optical drive may be supplied as a bolt-on external device. DVD writer drives are increasingly common in laptops and we recommend that you look for a device that handles both formats of media – DVD-RW and DVD+RW – and, ideally, supports double-capacity dual-layer discs.

This laptop has an integrated DVD writer.

Weighing it all up

Whichever manufacturer you choose, you'll likely find an extensive and probably bewildering range of models on offer – and that's before you consider optional extras like software bundles, hard drive upgrades, additional batteries and all the rest. The trick is finding a laptop that fits both your needs and your budget. For instance, do you need Bluetooth if you don't have any other Bluetooth-enabled devices (such as a PDA) to network with? Is Wi-Fi wireless networking a must for you? Do you want or need to burn DVDs on your laptop or would it suffice just to be able to play them? Are you planning to make this your main computer, in which case you'll want a desktop replacement, or is portability more important?

By way of example, we've plucked a few broadly representative models from a couple of manufacturers' ranges and shown them with their current prices (which will of course be out of date tomorrow, let alone when you read this). No matter: it serves to illustrate that design and pricing vary according to the features.

Model:	Acer TravelMate 2702WLMi
Price:	£880
Comment:	Powerful but heavy to lug around. This is primarily a business tool that, thanks to decent sound and video, could also serve as a desktop replacement for the family.

Processor	Pentium M (3.0GHz)
Memory	512MB
Hard drive	40GB
Optical drive	Internal DVD writer
Screen	15.4-inch, widescreen
Video outputs	VGA
Battery life	1 hour
PC Card	1 x Type II
USB	4 ports
FireWire	No
Modem	Yes
Wired networking	10/100Mb/sec
Wireless networking	802.11g
Bluetooth	No
Weight	3.4kg

Model:	Acer TravelMate 382TMi
Price:	£1174
Comment:	A Centrino-based ultra-portable system with a small screen and no internal drive. This is aimed at the traveller for whom portability and battery life matter most. Wireless networking is on hand for hooking up with hotspots.

Processor	Intel Pentium M (1.6GHz)
Memory	512MB
Hard drive	60GB
Optical drive	External DVD writer
Screen	12.1-inch
Video outputs	VGA
Battery life	4.5 hours
PC Card	1 x Type II
USB	2 ports
FireWire	Yes
Modem	Yes
Wired networking	10/100Mb/sec
Wireless networking	802.11g
Bluetooth	No
Weight	1.6kg

Model:	Acer Aspire 1362LC
Price:	£633
Comment:	Dull, but very good value, system for the home.

Processor	AMD Sempron 2800+
Memory	256MB
Hard drive	40GB
Optical drive	Internal CD-RW/DVD-ROM combination
Screen	15-inch
Video outputs	VGA and TV-out (S-video)
Battery life	3 hours
PC Card	2 x Type II or 1 x Type III
USB	4 ports
FireWire	Yes
Modem	Yes
Wired networking	10/100Mb/sec
Wireless networking	802.11g
Bluetooth	No
Weight	3.6kg

Model:	Acer 1804WSMi
Price:	£1198
Comment:	A thoroughbred desktop replacement with super-fast networking, huge screen and Bluetooth. It has a lousy battery life but this hardly matters as it's almost too heavy to take anywhere!

Processor	Intel Pentium 4 (3.2GHz)
Memory	512MB
Hard drive	80GB
Optical drive	Internal DVD writer
Screen	17-inch widescreen
Video outputs	VGA and TV-out (S-video)
Battery life	1 hour
PC Card	1 x Type II with pre-installed card reader
USB	4 ports
FireWire	Yes
Modem	Yes
Wired networking	10/100/1000Mb/sec
Wireless networking	802.11g
Bluetooth	Yes
Weight	4.5kg

Model:	Acer Ferrari 3400LMi
Price:	£1550
Comment:	Markedly similar specification to the 1804WSMi but considerably lighter (thanks in part to the smaller screen). It's also £350 more expensive.

Processor	Mobile AMD Athlon 64 3000+
Memory	512MB
Hard drive	80GB
Optical drive	Internal DVD writer
Screen	15-inch
Video outputs	VGA, TV-out (S-video)
Battery life	3 hours
PC Card	1 x Type II with pre-installed card reader
USB	4 ports
FireWire	Yes
Modem	Yes
Wired networking	10/100/1000Mb/sec
Wireless networking	802.11g
Bluetooth	Yes
Weight	3.01kg

Model:	Advent 7060
Price:	£600
Comment:	Heavy, relatively underpowered but impressively cheap. This might make a reasonable desktop replacement system for the home but the lack of wireless networking is a shame.

Processor	Intel Celeron (2.8GHz)
Memory	256MB
Hard drive	40GB
Optical drive	Internal DVD writer
Screen	15-inch
Video outputs	VGA, TV-out (S-video)
Battery life	2 hours
PC Card	1 x Type II
USB	2 ports
FireWire	Yes
Modem	Yes
Wired networking	10/100Mb/sec
Wireless networking	No
Bluetooth	No
Weight	3.8kg

Model:	Advent 7066M
Price:	£800
Comment:	Less than half the weight of the Advent 7060 but better equipped in most respects, this is an attractively priced ultra-portable.

Processor	Intel Celeron M (1.5GHz)
Memory	512MB
Hard drive	80GB
Optical drive	Internal DVD writer
Screen	12.1-inch
Video outputs	VGA, TV-out (S-video)
Battery life	2.4 hours
PC Card	1 x Type II
USB	2 ports
FireWire	Yes
Modem	Yes
Wired networking	10/100Mb/sec
Wireless networking	Yes
Bluetooth	No
Weight	1.7kg

PART

Tablet PCs

There's really not a great deal to say here. A Tablet PC is a laptop with a quirk, that quirk being that you can write on the screen and control menus and programs with an electronic pen.

Tablet PCs really come into their own for taking notes in a classroom or meeting, for annotating documents and for drawing, design and doodling. They can be held in one hand and scribbled on with the other, just like a (heavy and expensive) PDA. Voice recording and speech recognition also come as standard so you can record notes and interviews or dictate directly into a word processor. If, for instance, your work takes you on site visits, a Tablet PC may suit you for making notes as you walk around, particularly if you find the screen size of a PDA too limiting. They are also fantastic for web browsing, watching videos or playing music, and can be used in confined spaces, such as airline seats, when even a small laptop is cumbersome. Wireless networking is built-in. Tablets can be used in portrait or landscape mode to suit the task in hand and it's usually possible to 'dock' a slate-style device in order to connect a keyboard, a mouse and even a monitor. Bluetooth makes it easy to share files with a desktop system...

When the stock-taking gets you down, watch a movie instead on your Tablet PC.

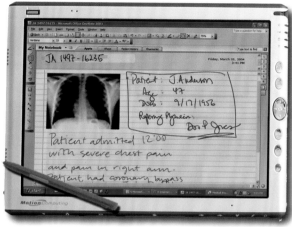

You can use a slate-style Tablet PC in portrait or landscape mode.

Tablet PC formats

But enough of the sales pitch. Commercial take-up of Tablet PCs has been slow, probably because the benefits are not immediately obvious except in niche circumstances. Do you really want to write on screen rather than use a keyboard? Even a slow typist can probably outpace somebody writing by hand and the thought of composing and editing a lengthy document with a pen rather than with a keyboard is daunting to many (present company included). Bear in mind too that your handwriting must be sufficiently legible and consistent for software to accurately transcribe it into text. Tablet PCs are also considerably more expensive than comparable laptops, although prices are at last beginning to drop.

There are two main types of Tablet PC. First up is the 'slate', in which there is no keyboard at all. This is the closest design to an oversized PDA, with control and data entry handled entirely with an electronic pen (or voice commands). Some standalone slates

can be 'docked' in a holder and controlled with a connected keyboard and mouse should the need arise.

And then we have the 'convertible' Tablet PC. This is more like a laptop with the difference that the display screen can be turned through 180 degrees and flipped over to transform the device into a slate. The keyboard is there when you want it and hidden when you don't. Naturally, these flexible convertibles tend to cost and weigh rather more than true slates.

An alternative convertible design features a keyboard that can be unplugged completely rather than hidden, to leave a detached slate-style display.

Tablet PCs run a special version of Windows called – you guessed it – Windows XP Tablet Edition 2005, which is designed specifically for pen input. There have been rumours that Microsoft will stop developing this system and ultimately scrap support for the Tablet platform but there's no hard evidence of this as we write.

Now you see it ... and now you don't (the keyboard, we mean). That's the beauty of a convertible.

Specifications

As for the hardware specifications, judge a Tablet PC much as you would judge a laptop i.e. weigh up processor types and speeds, memory, hard drive size and audio and video capability. To keep the weight down, CD and DVD drives are usually external and have to be connected via USB or FireWire. Here's a sample model.

Model:	HP Compaq tc1100
Price:	£1500
Comment:	This convertible has an optional, detachable keyboard (model PK225AA)

Processor	Intel Pentium M (1.1GHz)
Memory	512MB
Hard drive	40GB
Optical drive	None
Screen	10.4-inch
Video outputs	VGA
Battery life	Not specified but expect around 3–4 hours maximum
PC Card	2 x Type II or 1 x Type III
USB	2 ports
FireWire	No
Modem	Yes
Wired networking	10/100Mb/sec
Wireless networking	802.11g
Bluetooth	Yes
Weight	1.4kg in slate mode; 1.8kg with the keyboard attached

Right for you?

If you are attracted by the concept of a Tablet PC, be it a slate or a convertible or something in between, we strongly recommend that you try out a few models before committing to a purchase. Look for display models in shops and insist on a hands-on demo. You may find that even a sleek slate is rather awkward and heavy, a bit like a glorified clipboard, or find pen-on-screen note-taking trickier than you imagined. They can also get rather warm and a touch noisy, with internal fans cooling an internal hard drive.

Or you might be instantly smitten. Tablet PCs certainly have their followers and they tend to be passionate in their enthusiasm.

Pen and paper live on in the Tablet PC ... but with digital ink. Note that a Tablet's pen is not a dumb plastic stylus like that of a PDA but rather a special electronic sensor that reacts with the touch-sensitive screen.

PART

Smartphones

There is yet another alternative to the PDA or laptop. While some PDAs also work as mobile telephones, first and foremost they are handheld computers. Indeed, you may feel a little silly holding a PDA to your ear. Well, a smartphone also combines telephone and computer functionality in a single device but it comes at it from the opposite direction. That is, a smartphone is a mobile telephone with additional PDA-style features.

Spot the difference

One key, defining difference between a PDA and a smartphone is that the latter has a keyboard. This can be a full but miniature QWERTY keyboard or a customised version of the same, or even just a telephone dialpad on which you can type characters in the same way as you would compose a text message. Regardless, the point is that you can enter text by typing rather than with a stylus. Smartphones also tend to be neater and lighter than PDAs, and have significantly smaller screens.

In fact, though, the differences between a PDA with mobile phone capability and a smartphone with computer pretensions are increasingly unimportant and, arguably, even meaningless. Pretty much all mobile phones are 'smart' and pretty much all PDAs either come with mobile phones built-in or can be adapted by means of a plug-in expansion module.

...whereas this one provides a miniature replica of a laptop keyboard. Forget touch-typing, though – this is a one-finger, one-key-at-a-time approach to data entry.

This mobile phone has a slide-out keyboard but it's by no means a full-blown QWERTY affair ...

Key features

So what should you look for in a smartphone? The first consideration has to be its network capability, by which we mean how and where it lets you make telephone calls and/or send text messages. There's little point spending upwards of £100 on a swanky smartphone that plays videos but stops taking calls the moment you take it overseas. See p.46–48 for the low-down on GSM.

Integrated cameras are *de rigueur* these days, meaning you can take photos on your smartphone and either send them to another compatible phone or, more likely, upload them to a PC for editing, storing and printing. Games are a given and you'll find that you can download hundreds (probably thousands) of games from the internet, either freely or for a small fee. Indeed, a smartphone (or a PDA) can make a passable games console, not quite up to the mark of a Gameboy or a Portable PlayStation but not that far off.

You will want a memory card expansion slot for storing data and transferring files that you want to access on the phone. Most smartphones can play music files so with adequate memory you won't need to carry a separate MP3 player to have music on the move. You can of course send and receive text messages on any smartphone but most also offer Multimedia Messaging Service (MMS). This lets you send pictures, sound and video clips along with text, such as a short video shot on your camera's own phone with voice-over narration.

PDA features such as a diary and a contact manager are assured but you may want to check compatibility with your desktop software when it comes to document management. For instance, will you be able to transfer a company report or an e-book to the phone for reading and editing while you travel? Allied to this is how to connect the smartphone to your computer. The main options are with a USB cable, through a wireless Bluetooth network connection or, less commonly, through a Wi-Fi network

A Bluetooth headset lets you use your Bluetooth mobile phone hands-free whilst driving, walking or posing.

connection. Bluetooth is the most convenient if you already have a Bluetooth network set up. It also means you can use a wireless headset, which is essential if you make or take calls while driving. Otherwise, for daily synchronisation, a cable connection is fine.

As we noted earlier, Palm PDAs all run Palm OS software and Pocket PCs run Microsoft Windows Mobile. Many smartphones also use one of these operating systems. However, the most popular platform for smartphones is actually another operating system that goes by the name of Symbian. This is what you'll find on Nokia and Sony Ericsson phones. Linux is also beginning to make an appearance in handheld devices. In truth, smartphone software used to be lousy but Palm, Windows Mobile and Symbian are all good platforms these days.

Beyond of all this are questions such as: do you want to be able to browse the web and send email, download news headlines and watch them on the train, or tune into live video clips on your mobile phone? These issues are partly determined by the phone's native capabilities and software but more importantly by which mobile networks it can access. This takes us into the realm of GPR and 3G networks, for which see p.47–48.

And then there's the question of design and styling, of the compromise between size and power, of handset pricing and network tariffs, and of whether the phone you want is available on the network you use. For a rant on this last point, see p.42.

Many smartphones run a scaled-down version of Windows, replete with a Start button and familiar menus.

The fancier the phone, the bigger it gets. Here we see a Sanyo S750 (left) and an SPV C500 side-by-side. See p.41 for further details.

Orange SPV M2000: *A 195g Windows Mobile device with a large screen and a slide-out QWERTY keyboard. It's a tri-band GSM/GPRS device with Bluetooth, Wi-Fi, web browsing, email, Office compatibility and more.*

A smartphone round-up

The range of mobile phones out there is quite staggering and models hit and quit the market every day (or so it seems). We can't so much as scratch the surface of today's current crop let alone predict what will be out by the time you finish reading this page. What we can do, however, is highlight a few of the important points of difference. Here are seven new, or newish, smartphones.

Panasonic x700: *'Clam-shell' styling with a camera, Bluetooth and tri-band GSM/GPRS capability. This smartphone runs the Symbian operating system and weighs in at a lightweight 107g.*

Orange SPV C500: *This is a tri-band GSM/GPRS Windows Mobile smartphone that weighs a mere 100g and is packed with features: web browsing, email, video and music playback, instant messaging, Java games, camera and more.*

PalmOne Treo 650: *Is it a phone? Is it a PDA? Both, in fact. The Treo 650 has built-in Bluetooth networking, a camera, an expansion slot for extra storage, and a miniature QWERTY keyboard. It's also a fully-featured Palm PC. GSM and GPRS but no 3G.*

NEC 338: *A humble-looking, budget 3G phone (also tri-band GSM and GPRS) that eschews Bluetooth, memory card expansion and other frills for the sake of price and weight (113g), but still manages to include a camera. The value here is in the 3G content, as provided by the 3 network with which this phone is exclusively linked.*

Sanyo S750: *A 3G smartphone with tri-band GSM and GPRS for backup. Note the detachable aerial and the slide-out keyboard for data entry, email and web browsing. It has a video/still camera, Bluetooth and USB and weighs 122g.*

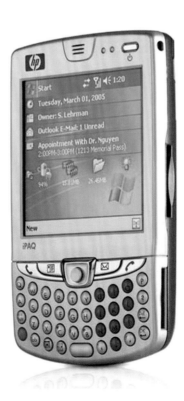

HP iPAQ Mobile Messenger: *If the Treo 650 is PalmOne's approach to smartphones, this is the equivalent contender from the Windows/Pocket PC stable. This model has the expected QWERTY keyboard, Bluetooth, camera, GSM/GPRS coverage and, just possibly, integrated GPS (see p.126). It's so new and cutting edge that HP wouldn't provide us with a high resolution picture but by the time you read this it'll probably come free with Frosties.*

A rant...

By and large, telephone network providers – Vodafone, Orange, 3, O2, T-Mobile and Virgin – sell mobile phones and by and large, in our opinion, they make an appalling fist of it. For years, handsets were discounted to the point of being free but the price was clawed back in impenetrable and often punitive monthly contracts, making that 'free' handset one of the most expensive gadgets on the planet once you started using it.

The balance has changed somewhat in the sense that you now usually have to pay something for the handset, but generally not its true value. The networks still seek to ensnare us in monthly contracts and bamboozle us with free call time and text messages here, exclusive content there, and ferocious penalties everywhere.

Worse, handsets may be 'locked' so that you can only use them on one particular network. Worse still from the perspective of free choice, not all handsets are available on all networks. It's perfectly possible to find that you can't get the phone you really want because the service provider that you favour simply doesn't sell it. Contrariwise, you might like Vodafone's range of handsets but discover that you can't pick up a Vodafone signal in your front room. A smartphone that calculates spreadsheet formulae but can't make a telephone call is pretty dumb.

In short, picking the right phone with the right network at the right price is little short of impossible. These waters muddy further when you come to consider GPRS and 3G networks where live internet-style content is available on mobile phones but services are billed not by the time spent 'online' but by the amount of data downloaded. We'll look at these networks in Part 3.

... and a reality check

In principle, there's nothing to stop a hardware manufacturer coming up with the 'perfect' smartphone. It would have:

- Quad-band GSM
- GPRS
- EDGE
- 3G
- Bluetooth
- Wi-Fi
- GPS
- A large screen
- A QWERTY keyboard
- Games and applications
- Modular expansion possibilities (i.e. plug-in cards)
- Plenty of memory

Indeed, the Treo and iPAQ Mobile Messenger ranges are just about there already. But here's the real dilemma. While manufacturers will always find ways to shrink technology, a truly smart phone is always going to be bigger and bulkier than a regular handset. Do you really want to carry a fairly hefty device like a Treo with you everywhere you go? Yet at the same time, a

There's no question about it: mobile technology is shrinking apace. But there comes a point where a device is either too small to use in comfort or too big to be truly portable.

Treo is not really big *enough*. Those microscopic QWERTY keyboards are tricky to use, even with good eyesight, and a Treo is simply not suited to large-scale data entry (any more than is a PDA with its stylus). A smartphone can in principle function as a powerful handheld computer, but in practice it's a nuisance.

So where does that leave us? On one hand, we want our mobile devices to be smart enough to do anything and small enough to take anywhere but, on the other hand, miniaturisation creates all manner of usability problems. Convergence is clever but does it actually produce devices that we can and want to use in the real world? Perhaps, just perhaps, the search for a truly unified mobile device that does absolutely everything is simply misplaced.

And we're not even going to mention the dread possibility of losing your Swiss Army smartphone and realising that your contacts, email, diary and novel-in-progress have disappeared with it, forever ...

Thanks to AVA Photographic, Swindon and the **museum-of-computing.org.uk**

PART **3**

MOBILE TECHNOLOGY MANUAL

Getting – and staying – in touch

PART  # Mobile networks explained

Or, at least, described. There are three main types of mobile telephone network around right now with others in the pipeline. One of your first and certainly most important decisions when shopping for a mobile phone – or a PDA with a telephone component, or a plug-in mobile module, or an accessory for a laptop – should be how the device will make and receive calls. It's pretty dry stuff so we'll keep this as brief as possible.

GSM

To make a telephone call from a mobile phone, you connect to a digital cellular network using Global System for Mobile communications (GSM) technology and send packets of data to and fro across the airwaves. Or rather your phone does. GSM networks (also known as 2G or second-generation networks) are operational in something like 200 countries, which means that you can take your phone abroad and use it much as normal. However, a couple of considerations apply:

● Your network provider – Vodafone, Orange or whoever – must enable 'roaming' on your handset and billing account. This is a formality these days but it always pays to check that roaming is enabled before you leave. Without roaming, your mobile phone will be unable to connect to a network overseas.
 Your network provider must also have at least one network partner in the country or countries that you are visiting. Check its website for coverage. Bear in mind that you will be billed heavily every time you use your phone overseas because you must pay both the local network's fees plus those of your own network. On the other hand, the convenience of taking both your handset and your mobile number with you probably makes this worthwhile. Anybody calling your mobile number will track you down wherever you wander. Even if you're out of reach of a network, you can pick up voicemail messages later.

● GSM operates at different radio frequencies in different parts of the world. In Europe, Asia and Australia, it operates at either 900MHz or 1800MHz. Virtually all mobile phones are 'dual-band', which means they can switch between these frequencies as required. In the US and Canada, the predominant frequency is 1900MHz, but some areas, including Central America, use 850MHz instead. A 'tri-band' mobile works at 900, 1800 or 1900MHz and is thus well suited for widespread travel (every smartphone we looked at on p.40–41 is tri-band). But only a quad-band phone throws 850MHz into the mix and thus completes the picture.
 On a GSM network, you can make and receive calls and send and receive text messages. If your handset has a modem, you can also dial an internet account to access email and WAP sites.

It pays to check network coverage before you travel abroad. You may, for instance, find that you need to upgrade your handset to dual-band or triple-band model, or even have to change networks if your current network offers only patchy coverage or none whatsoever.

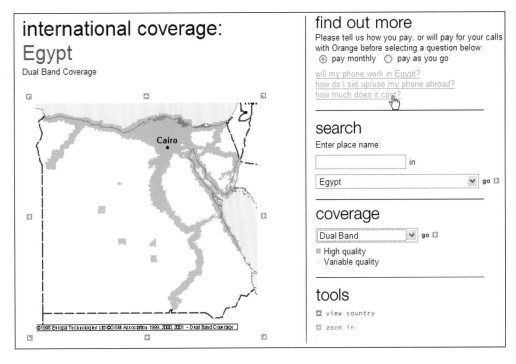

However, web access is dismally slow over GSM. In fact, it's barely worth the bother.

GPRS

Next up, we find General Packet Radio Services (GPRS, also known as 2.5G). A GPRS network allows a compatible handset to retain a more or less permanent connection to a relatively fast service, akin to an always-on broadband internet connection. GPRS has widespread domestic and international coverage.

The importance of GPRS to the mobile worker is significant:

● The connection is about 10 times 'faster' than GSM, which means that it's much more suitable for sending and receiving relatively large quantities of data. Internet access over GPRS may be slow but it works.

● You can connect a laptop or a PDA to a GPRS handset via infrared, Bluetooth or a USB cable connection in order to access the internet. For instance, you can check email, browse the web, use instant messaging, download files and so forth on a laptop that is wirelessly connected to the internet via a GPRS-enabled mobile handset.

● You can send multimedia messages which go far beyond the 160-character text-only constraints of normal SMS messaging.

● If a GPRS signal is not available, the handset will (or should) fall back upon GSM and so still function as a phone.

Because a GPRS network is always on, subject to signal strength, it is impractical for network providers to bill you for the time you spend 'online'. Instead, they bill on the basis of how much data you send and receive over the network. This, needless to say, is impossible to gauge upfront, although you can take it as read that downloading music, pictures or video will end up costing you a pretty penny. Most GPRS users enjoy their new-found access-anywhere approach to the internet with enthusiastic abandon for a month or so – and then have to pick themselves up when the first bill arrives with a thump.

Internet and email access virtually anywhere courtesy of GPRS. Just watch those bills mount up ...

Here's a dual GPRS/3G PC Card for laptops ...

3G

Universal Mobile Telecommunications System (UMTS) is the basis for what we are used to calling 3G. Like GPRS, it's an always-on connection. It runs at a top theoretical speed of 1920 Kilobits per second (Kb/sec) but networks aim to provide users with a baseline connection of around 384Kb/sec. If you consider that a dial-up modem gives you at best a 56Kb/sec connection and an entry-level broadband connection around 500Kb/sec, you can see that 3G is really fairly fast. This means you can do rather more on your mobile phone. Possibilities include:

● Fast web surfing.
● Instant email everywhere.
● Talking face-to-face in video calls with people who have compatible handsets ('Say hello to Gran, kids ... but quickly, because this is costing Daddy a fortune!').
● Streaming high-quality audio and reasonable-quality video to your phone, with the option to download and buy songs and clips.
● Live news alerts, sports scores, interviews, traffic reports, etc.
● Using the handset as a modem to connect a laptop or PDA to the internet. Bolt-on 3G expansion cards are also available for laptops and PDAs so you don't necessarily need a 3G mobile phone to stay online as you travel.
● Seamless interoperability with other networks and global roaming as 3G networks spring – okay, limp – into action around the world.

An alternative to UMTS is called EDGE – Enhanced Data Rates for GSM Evolution (now *there's* a tortuous acronym for you). EDGE technology essentially speeds up a GSM/GPRS network to the point where it qualifies for the label 'third-generation', i.e. it can achieve data transfer rates in excess of 384Kbits/sec. However, although EDGE has proven popular in the US and is supported by many PDAs and smartphones, Europe in general has followed the UMTS path to high-speed mobile networks.

3G has been notoriously slow off the mark and coverage is still patchy in the UK. However, networks are now available and there are some decent introductory offers. For instance, Orange currently offers up to 50MB of data transfers per month for a fixed fee. This equates to:

● Downloading 60 minutes of film clips
● Viewing 3000 web pages
● Sending and receiving 20,000 emails

One point worth making is that something interesting happens as you cross the bridge from GPRS to 3G. GPRS basically makes internet access possible and easy on a mobile device. You can, for instance, log onto websites designed to be viewed on small screens or surreptitiously Google the answers to questions during a pub quiz. To this extent, GPRS is an enabling technology. But with the advent of 3G, network providers are now intent on 'pushing' content to you i.e. sending music, video, messages and more to your phone. You merely have to subscribe to a service once and then sit back and wait for an endless stream of killer content to be delivered seamlessly to your device. A mobile phone becomes less of an active tool and more of a passive gateway.

Obviously enough, the network providers want you to use 3G. Having paid billions for the licences to operate the networks in the first place, they really, *really* want you to use 3G. How happily they will bill you for every bit and byte of data. But will you sign up? That's the £22 billion question. See p.145–147.

... just slot it in place for high-speed internet access over a wireless telephone network. No mobile phone required. Similar expansion cards are available for PDAs.

PART ③ Email on a PDA

Let's say you have a PDA and you need access to email while out and about. The method you choose depends on where you are and how urgent it is that messages are sent and received without delay. Here are some ideas to consider. We'll consider another on p.61.

Here's a modem from Socket (**www.socketcom.com**) that connects to a Pocket PC wirelessly via Bluetooth. Just plug it into a phone socket and dial up an internet account.

Plug a modem into your PDA and get yourself connected.

An 802.11b Wi-Fi card in the SDIO format. This lets you connect your PDA to a wireless hotspot.

Keeping connected

● The simplest system is to handle email as part of the synchronisation process. Every time you synchronise the PDA with a host PC, the contents of the PDA's Outbox are sent to the host PC, at which point the messages are sent using the host PC's usual mail program. If there have been any new messages received on the host PC since the previous synchronisation, they will be downloaded to the PDA's Inbox at the same time.

● If you spend a lot of time away from your PC and synchronise only occasionally, or if you frequently need to use email while you're out-and-about, the answer might be to send and receive email directly from the PDA. For this, you'll need a mobile phone with a built-in modem. Connect this to the Pocket PC with a cable (or wirelessly with Bluetooth or infrared) and you'll be able to dial up an internet connection. You can then either access the same email account that you use on your desktop system or use a dedicated account just for your PDA.

● If you don't own a sophisticated mobile phone, you can send and receive email from any PDA using a hard-wired or wireless modem plugged into one of its expansion slots. In the case of a wireless modem, you'll need a wireless receiver plugged into a nearby phone socket.

● If your PDA itself functions as a mobile telephone, you can dial up to the internet directly.

● You can install a Wi-Fi expansion card to join a public wireless hotspot (see p.59) or use an Ethernet card to hook up to a wired home or business network. Either way, you can share the network's internet connection.

For simplicity, you might like to use a webmail account with your PDA. This can be accessed with the PDA's browser whenever an internet connection is available. The downside of retrieving email directly to your PDA is that messages are not automatically reconciled with messages on your desktop PC, which means that you'll have to get used to managing two separate accounts.

Unless your bills are being paid by your employer, the high cost of internet access over a mobile phone might be enough to dissuade you from all of this. On the plus side, you have total freedom to roam almost anywhere in the world without losing touch with your Inbox.

Dialling up with a Pocket PC

By way of example, let's get online and access an email account with a Pocket PC and a modem. It's a fiddly business but one you may well find worthwhile.

If the modem you'll be using is the one in your mobile phone, ensure that Bluetooth is enabled on your Pocket PC and that the mobile phone is switched on. In Bluetooth Manager, tap New and, on the following screen, select 'Connect to Internet via phone'. Follow the instructions in the Bluetooth Connection Wizard to establish a partnership between your Pocket PC and your phone. See p.165 for more on this.

To configure the modem connection, open the Start menu, tap Settings, then select the Connections tab. Tap the Connections icon and select 'Add a new modem connection'. This leads to a screen on which you enter a name for the connection (anything you like that means something to you) and choose the type of modem you'll be using. In the example 'Bluetooth dial-up modem' has been selected, but the same procedures work for IrDA and serial devices. Tap Next.

On the next screen, enter the dial-up number of your ISP exactly as it should be dialled, including the area code. Tap Next. This leads you to the screen shown here, where you enter your user name and password. These are the same details that you would use on a desktop PC to make a dial-up networking connection to your ISP. You do not need to enter a domain unless your ISP specifically supplies one. Tap Finish and then tap OK to close the Connections screen.

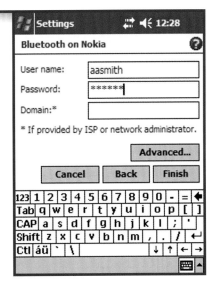

To configure your email account, tap Messaging on the Start menu. Now tap the Accounts menu and select New Account. On setup Screen 1 (of 5), enter your email address and tap Next. Wait a few seconds on Screen 2 while the account is automatically configured. You'll see the message 'Connecting...', which will eventually change to 'Completed'. Tap Next.

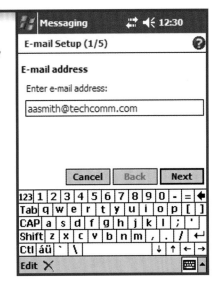

On Screen 3, enter your full name as you wish it to appear in the From box on your emails, plus the user name supplied by your ISP and your password. Tap the 'Save password' box, then click Next.

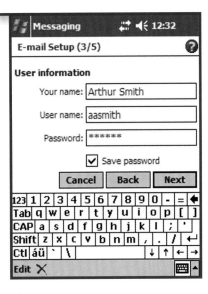

On Screen 4, select the email account type. This will probably be POP3, though IMAP4 is offered as an alternative. Give the account a unique name, which can be anything that means something to you. The name will be used to identify the email folders used by this account on the Pocket PC. Tap Next.

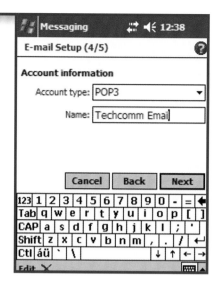

On Screen 5, enter the names of the incoming and outgoing mail servers as provided by your ISP. Again, leave the Domain field blank. If you then tap the Options button you can customise various aspects of the email service including how often messages are checked and how much of each message is downloaded. To accept the default settings, click Finish. You'll then be asked if you want to download mail for this new account now. Tap Yes.

Once you've established your new email account, you can start using it by tapping Messaging on the Start menu, just as you do when you want to use your synchronised Outlook email. You'll find a completely separate set of email folders for each email account you set up. Switch between them by opening the Accounts menu and selecting the one you want to use. If a connection is not made automatically, tap Connect (also on the Accounts menu).

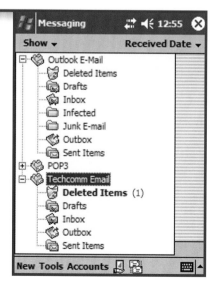

Getting online with GPRS

If your mobile phone is GPRS- or 3G-enabled, you won't have to dial up, log on and log off every time you want to browse the web or access email. However, you might prefer to use a PDA's larger screen and marginally less fiddly input methods for reading and writing messages. In this case, the trick is to connect the PDA to the mobile phone and use the latter's network connection.

Which is fine, except that sharing GPRS internet access with a PDA is no simple matter. In fact, HP provides no detailed information about GPRS connectivity in its iPAQ user guides. The best place to turn for help is your mobile phone service provider. O_2, for example, provides detailed instructions on how to connect a Pocket PC to a POP3 email service over GPRS on its support web pages (see **web.o2.ie/personal/help**). Scroll down and click on 'Pocket PC GPRS User Guides'.

Of course, you can also connect a laptop to the internet using a mobile phone and a GPRS connection. And if you have a 3G handset, you can benefit from greater bandwidth.

The first step is persuading the phone and the laptop to recognise and talk to one another. Here's what the process looks like using Bluetooth and an Orange GPRS handset.

Ask your mobile network provider for help configuring shared internet access over GPRS. Here's O_2's helpful offering.

On the laptop, open Control Panel, then Network and Internet Connections and look for the Bluetooth icon. Click this. Just to state the obvious, you won't see this option unless your laptop has Bluetooth capability.

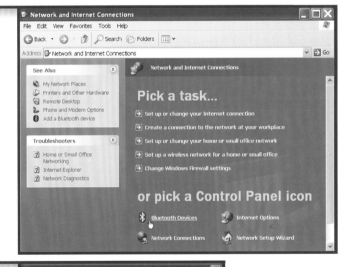

Bluetooth networking works on the basis of voluntary 'discovery', by which means any two consenting devices can establish a partnership and share information and services. In the Options tab, enable discovery on the laptop. Then enable Bluetooth on the mobile phone and similarly switch to discovery mode.

On the laptop, open the Devices tab, click Add, and click Next when the wizard launches. Your laptop will now search for other Bluetooth devices within range. So long as the phone is in discovery mode, they should find one another.

Success. The laptop has found the mobile phone and is ready to establish a Bluetooth partnership. Select the phone icon and click Next to proceed.

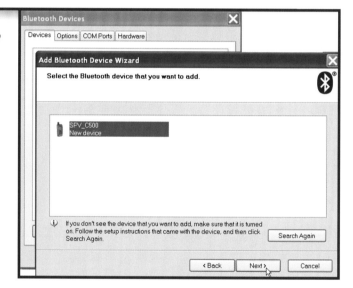

Bluetooth networks can and should be secured to prevent unauthorised access. You may have to use a specific passkey if the mobile phone's manual says so, or you may be able to choose your own or let Windows generate one automatically. Try the automatic route first.

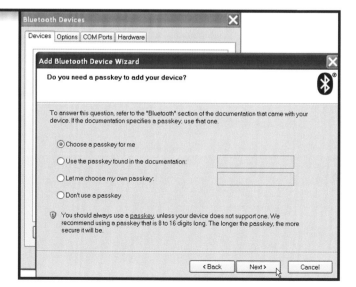

When you see this screen, check your mobile phone's display. There should be a prompt to enter the security code or passkey. Do so now and the devices will be instantly 'paired'. You only have to go through these steps once; next time the laptop and phone are turned on with Bluetooth enabled within 10 metres of each other, they should pair-up automatically.

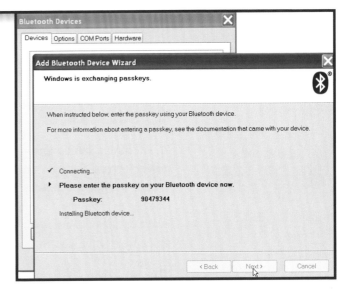

The tricky bit is now persuading the laptop to use the phone's GPRS network service as if it was a dial-up internet connection. For this, return to Network and Internet Connections in Control Panel and run the New Connection Wizard. However, you'll have to enter some obscure information along the way – initialisation strings and the like – and only your network service provider (Orange, in this example) can provide the details.

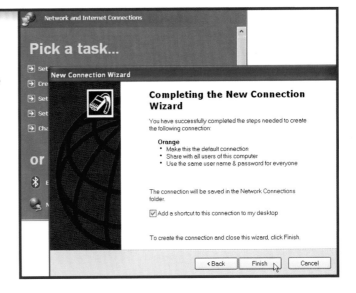

Ultimately, you'll end up with a Network Connections icon which lets you access the phone's GPRS network connection and hence the internet. This operates just like a dial-up networking connection to an ISP, albeit one that doesn't require a telephone number, a user name or a password.

PART 3 Email access around the world

If you have a laptop and need internet access as you travel, particularly to send and receive email, using your mobile's modem is one option but by no means the only one. Here we'll glance at three alternatives. But first, a word on making sure that your email account remains accessible while you travel.

Email strategy

The easiest way to send and receive email from anywhere in the world is, of course, to use a web-based service like Gmail (**www.gmail.com**) or Hotmail (**www.hotmail.com**). All you need is an internet connection and a device capable of running a web browser. Web-based email, or webmail, is completely independent of any Internet Service Provider. All you need to remember is your email address and your password.

However, the chances are that your main, or even sole, email address is currently something like **yourname@yourisp.co.uk**, i.e. an email address supplied by your Internet Service Provider. You probably also send and receive messages with a program like Outlook or Outlook Express while you are connected to the internet via that ISP from home. But when you travel, you'll need to use an alternative means of getting online and you may not have access to your usual software. What to do?

Log into your ISP's email account from any device – desktop, laptop, PDA or smartphone – that has access to the internet and a web browser.

clara.net

| Create Message | | | | | | kyle@scunnered.co.uk |

| Folders | | Create Message | | Preferences | | Address Book | | FAQ | | Log Out |

| **Address Book:** | To: | Cc: | Bcc: |

To: you@coldplace.home

Cc:

Bcc:

Reply-To:

Subject: Greetings from abroad!

Message:
Hi all

Just a quick update. I'm currently in

If your ISP lets you down on the webmail front, check for messages with mail2web.

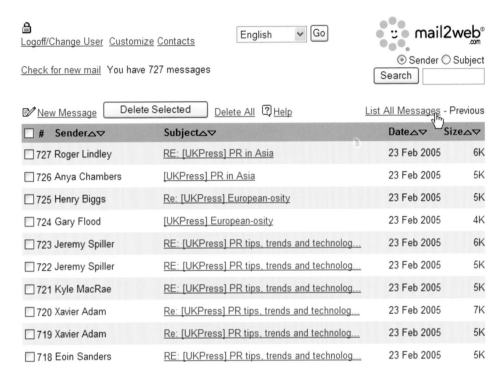

Well, most ISPs now offer web access to email. This means you can log into your email Inbox from a web page using a browser and, from there, read, compose and send messages. Before you travel, be sure to make a note of this web page's address, together with your login name (probably just your email address) and your password. Also test the service before you leave.

If your ISP doesn't provide its own webmail service, no matter: use the free and rather brilliant mail2web service to access your email. This can be found at **www.mail2web.com**.

One thing to remember is that ISP-provided email inboxes have size limitations. Once you have received a given quantity of data, sometimes as low as 5MB, all further incoming messages are bounced back to the sender. A single email with a largish file attachment can completely block your inbox. It is important, therefore, to regularly delete messages that you no longer need. If you want to keep them for later reference, forward them to a secondary Gmail account before deleting them from your Inbox. You can then retrieve these messages from Gmail at any time. Gmail provides a welcome 1GB of storage per account so you're highly unlikely to fill it up even on a round-the-world trip.

Alternatively, set up a temporary filter on your ISP email account to forward all incoming messages directly to a Gmail or similar webmail account. This will keep your Inbox completely clear and so sidestep size restrictions. Not all ISPs let you set up filters, however, so check this out well in advance.

Public internet access: internet cafés

Perhaps the most obvious approach is popping into an internet café and paying for internet access on a desktop computer by the minute or hour. Such establishments can be found in virtually all cities and major towns. You'll find dedicated operations run by major chains like easyinternetCafé and local entrepreneurs with ancient PCs in corners of side-street shops. Local libraries sometimes also offer internet access (sometimes for free), as do hotels (always for a fee), and you'll find pay-per-minute standalone internet kiosks located in train stations, airports and shops.

From café to kiosk, internet access points are widely available

Public internet access: wireless hotspots

Wireless hotspots: now there's a buzz phrase for you. A hotspot is an area where a wireless network offers internet access to fee-paying subscribers. To get connected, your laptop, PDA or smartphone must be equipped with a Wi-Fi adapter. This will then 'tune in' to the network and allow you to connect with a login name and password. These are supplied by the service provider in exchange for cash. The more you pay, the longer you can stay online.

You'll find hotspots in hotels, airports, coffee shops, bars and an ever-growing variety of locations. To find a hotspot near you or in a location you intend to visit, try **www.wi-fihotspotlist.com**. Again, it's wise to give your hardware a trial run at a local hotspot before travelling further afield, especially if you intend to rely heavily on this method for your internet access.

As wireless hotspots develop, they are sure to offer GPRS and, increasingly, 3G connectivity as well as Wi-Fi. Bluetooth is another possibility. This means that you may well have a choice to make concerning how you get online and how you pay the bills. The usual pricing models are time spent online, with Wi-Fi/Bluetooth, and quantity of data transferred, with GPRS/3G.

Tap into the internet wirelessly with a Wi-Fi hotspot.

The Definitive WiFi HotSpot Directory

Displaying results within 1 miles of center of Glasgow, GB
27 HotSpots found, showing 1 - 25
Result Pages: 1 2

WiFi Hotspot Location	Hotspot Address	Wireless Networks
Scottish Enterprise	5 Atlantic Quay Broomielaw, Glasgow, G2 8LU, United Kingdom	BT Openzone
Ramada Jarvis	201 Ingram Street, Glasgow, G1 1DQ, United Kingdom	BT Openzone
O'neills Glasgow (queen St)	157 Queen Street, Glasgow, G1 3BJ, United Kingdom	mycloud
BT Openzone Payphone	West George Street, Glasgow, SC, G2 1BP, United Kingdom	BT Openzone
Caffe Nero (glasgow - St Vincent)	57-61 St Vincent Street, Glasgow, G2 5TB, United Kingdom	Trustive
Caffe Nero (Glasgow - St Vincent)	57-61 St Vincent Street, Glasgow, G2 5TB, United Kingdom	Boingo
Goose On Union Street	40-48 Union Street, Glasgow, G1 3QX, United Kingdom	BT Openzone
Goose On Union Street	40-48 Union Street, Glasgow, G1 3QX, United Kingdom	BT Openzone
Goose On Union Street Glasgow	46 Union Street, Glasgow, G1 3QX, United Kingdom	mycloud
BT Streetzone	Union Street, Glasgow, SC, G1 3TA, United Kingdom	BT Openzone
Horseshoe Bar	17-21 Drury Street, Glasgow, G2 5AE, United Kingdom	BT Openzone
78 St. Vincent	78 St Vincent Street, Glasgow, G2 5UB, United Kingdom	Boingo
Caffe Nero (Glasgow)	106 Union Street, Glasgow, G1 3QW, United Kingdom	Boingo

Trackdown a hotspot at home or abroad with **www.wi-fihotspotlist.com**. It's also worth trying a Google search for 'hotspot' or 'wi-fi' plus the name of your destination.

Global roaming dial-up

Many national and international hotels now provide broadband lines in bedrooms, usually for an exorbitant fee. Some also have wireless hotspots on offer in lounges and foyers. For the former, you need an Ethernet port on your laptop and a cable with RJ-45 plugs on both ends (i.e. a standard Ethernet cable); for the latter, a Wi-Fi adapter.

However, there may be times when you have to fall back upon a dial-up connection, such as when staying with friends or temporarily sharing an office. If your laptop or PDA has it's own internal modem or if you carry an external model, you can plug it into a standard analogue phone line and make a dial-up connection to an ISP.

But there are a couple of flies in this ointment for the overseas traveller:

- You may well need an adapter or cable that converts the country's telephone socket standard into an RJ-11 connection that works with your modem. If you travel widely, you'll benefit from a kit that provides a wide selection of adapters.
- If you unplug the telephone in your hotel room to use that line, you'll be billed to the tune of £1000 per hour, or something equally absurd, for the privilege of making a long-distance call. Why long distance? Because you need to connect to an ISP to get internet access and the only ISP with whom you have an account is based in the UK.
- You cannot connect an analogue modem (i.e. any modem designed for dial-up internet access) to a digital telephone system. Indeed, trying to do so may irreparably damage it. However, if a hotel is big enough to have installed an internal digital system, it should also be able to offer an analogue line for internet access. Check before you connect.

It would be better all round if you could call a local ISP regardless of where you happen to be. That's where a service like Netaway comes in handy.

Netaway taps into an established network of international ISP facilities. First, you download and install a dialler program on your laptop and then you buy some call credit upfront. You then tell the dialler where you are and it displays a list of local ISP numbers. If you find yourself in the south of France, for instance, you can dial-up Marseille, Montpellier or Nice for pay-as-you-go internet access; if you're in Japan, you'll find numbers from Akita to Yokohama.

On top of the local rate call charges, for which you will be billed by whoever owns the telephone line, Netaway deducts a flat fee of 8p per minute. This is deducted from your credit balance.

Coverage currently extends to 105 countries but check whether the service is suitable for you before you travel. See **www.netaway.com/access_numbers.html**.

Similar services are offered by:

Net2Roam	**www.net2roam**
Dial Media Group	**www2.dialmediagroup.com/global-roaming/default.asp**
Jetset	**www.jetsetroam.co.uk**

Alternatively, if you plan to spend some considerable time in one location, it may be cheaper to sign up with a local ISP on a pay-as-you-go basis. This way, you'll pay only the local call charges.

Don't forget to pack telephone adapters so that you can connect your modem to the local telephone socket.

Netaway provides local rate internet access wherever you roam. Even with an 8p per minute charge on top of the cost of the call, it's a whole lot cheaper than calling a UK ISP at international rates.

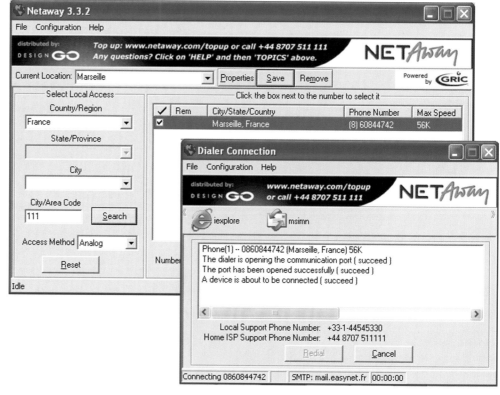

PART 3 Dedicated mobile email

As we have seen, it's possible to use a mobile phone's GPRS or 3G network connection to access the internet and email wirelessly while on the move. If your PDA has a mobile module, you can do the same directly; and if you can connect a mobile phone to a laptop, you can bring the internet to a larger screen and keyboard for greater ease of use. But it's all a bit complex.

When you think about what you actually want in the way of mobile communication rather than what's potentially achievable, you may discover that your needs are actually very simple. In fact, you may figure that you don't really need a handheld computer at all. Perhaps your needs boil down to this:
- A mobile phone
- Easy email access
- Occasional internet access
- A basic calendar, contacts book and note-taking tool

So why don't they make a gadget that's designed primarily for email? In fact, they do.

The BlackBerry 7100v has a proprietary operating system (no Windows here, thank you very much) designed primarily to make mobile email easy.

Some BlackBerry models, like this 7250, have full QWERTY keyboards. However, it's considerably less appealing to use as a mobile phone than the sleeker 7100 design.

Enter the BlackBerry

The BlackBerry device that we're considering here, a 7100v model on the UK Vodafone network, is a GSM/GPRS mobile phone with Bluetooth networking, a web browser, access to Vodafone's Live! online content and a bunch of useful applications including a contact manager and diary. However, its real *raison d'être* is to keep you in touch with your Inbox when you travel away from the desk – and it does this superbly. You can read new messages within minutes of them being sent and send your own email immediately over the wireless network. The device has an innovative keyboard that's basically a customised QWERTY design with some pairing-up of characters. It's surprisingly easy to use, even with a thumb, and an advanced SMS-style predictive text feature called SureType helps to cut down on the key presses. A scroll wheel on the side navigates through menus and makes selections, and a secondary button works as a back button.

BlackBerry email is a 'push' technology, which means that messages arrive on your device automatically without you having to do anything tedious like connecting to an ISP or accessing a webmail page. Email is 'just there', instantly, in your pocket, wherever you go. In fact, of all the gadgets that we looked at in the preparation of this book, the BlackBerry is the one that most immediately grabbed us and the one we were most reluctant to part with!

For years, BlackBerrys were designed for corporate types with big budgets, dedicated email servers and clued-up support teams. However, with the release of the 7100 and similar devices, this is changing in favour of the self-funding consumer with simpler requirements. BlackBerry software – which is after all the clever bit – is also finding its way into PDAs and smartphones, and competing companies are implementing similar push email technology. In short, BlackBerry email, or something very like it, will come to a mobile device near you soon.

Basic BlackBerry configuration

In this example, we'll use a BlackBerry 7100 model. This device operates on the GPRS network (with a fallback to GSM when necessary) and so has an always-on network connection.

Email access is configured via the Vodafone website at **www.mobileemail.vodafone. net**. *You'll be asked to enter the handset's PIN and IMEI numbers, both of which are printed on the inside of the case underneath the battery.*

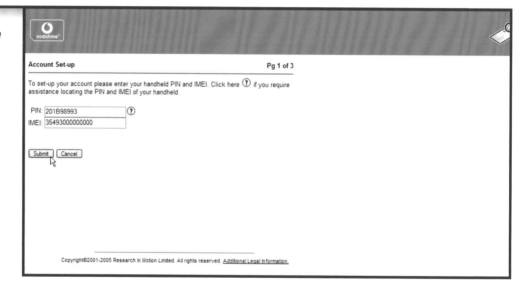

Account Set-up   Pg 1 of 3

To set-up your account please enter your handheld PIN and IMEI. Click here ⑦ if you require assistance locating the PIN and IMEI of your handheld.

PIN: 201B98993 ⑦
IMEI: 35493000000000

[Submit] [Cancel]

Copyright©2001-2005 Research In Motion Limited. All rights reserved. Additional Legal Information.

Now click the Create New Account button to set up an account with a login name and a password. You can also choose a BlackBerry email address. This done, you can log into the site.

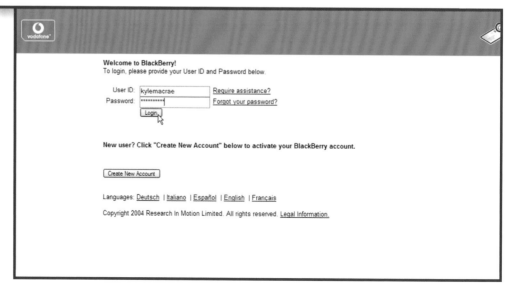

Welcome to BlackBerry!
To login, please provide your User ID and Password below.

User ID: kylemacrae   Require assistance?
Password: **********   Forgot your password?
[Login]

New user? Click "Create New Account" below to activate your BlackBerry account.

[Create New Account]

Languages: Deutsch | Italiano | Español | English | Français

Copyright 2004 Research In Motion Limited. All rights reserved. Legal Information.

*At this point, only messages sent to your new BlackBerry address (e.g. **kylemacrae@ mobileemail.vodafone.net**) will be forwarded to your BlackBerry device. To add other email addresses, click the Email Accounts link.*

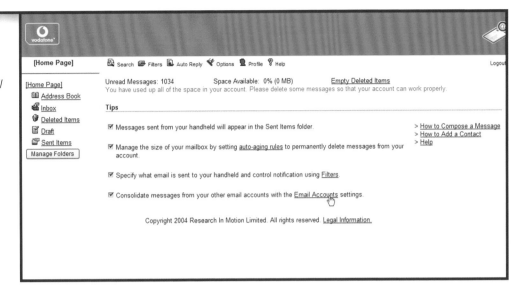

Click Add Account and supply the details that you use to access your ISP or other email address i.e. your login name and password. These details may have been supplied by your ISP when you first signed up.

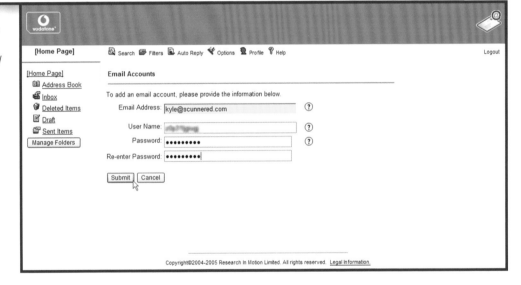

*If you have your own domain name and you use this for email (e.g. **yourname@yourdomain.com**), the same principles apply but the Vodafone web page needs some further information. In any case, if you see this screen select the first option and proceed.*

You now need to provide details of your email server. You'll find this information in the settings page of your usual desktop email program. If in doubt, ask your ISP. Check the 'leave messages on mail server' box (but see the note on p.66).

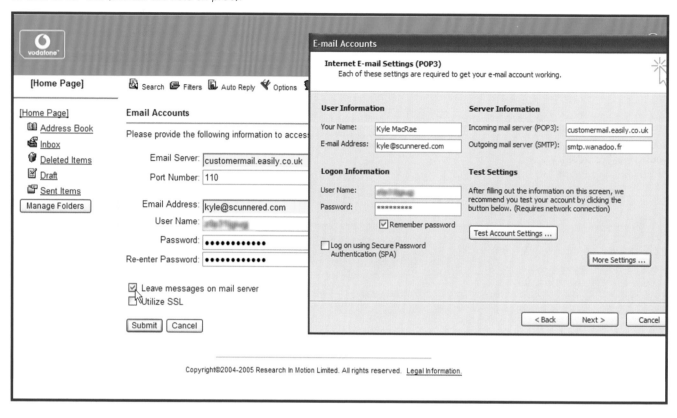

If you have several active email addresses, add them one by one in the same way. From now on, all new email sent to any of these addresses will automatically be delivered to your BlackBerry device – so long as it is connected to the Vodafone (or a roaming partner's) network – and stored in the webmail Inbox here.

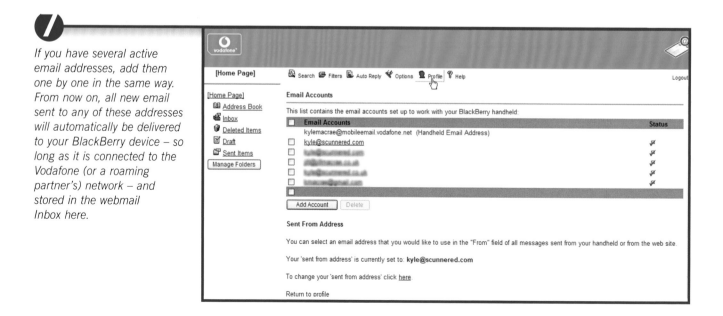

*Some useful options here. For instance, you can change your 'sent from' address. By default, when you send a message from your BlackBerry, the recipient will see your email address as the one you chose during registration (e.g. **kylemacrae@ mobileemail.vodafone.net**). If you would rather that messages seem to emanate from your usual email address (e.g. **yourname@yourdomain.com**), make the change here.*

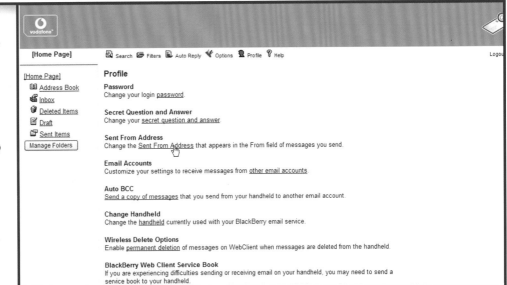

Now click the Wireless Delete Options link. By default, when you delete a message on your BlackBerry device, it is not deleted from your webmail Inbox. Unfortunately, this Inbox has only a 10MB storage capacity. When this limit is reached, fresh incoming email is simply bounced back to the sender. To save yourself having to manually purge your webmail Inbox, enable the permanent deletion option here. Now when you delete a message from the BlackBerry, it will also be deleted from the webmail Inbox.

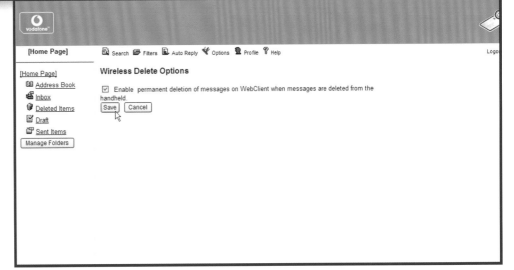

Here's what happens when you don't follow Step 9. Although we have deleted old messages on the BlackBerry itself, the web account is full and as a consequence no new messages can be received or delivered to the device. In other words, the BlackBerry stops working until you visit the web account and permanently delete old messages.

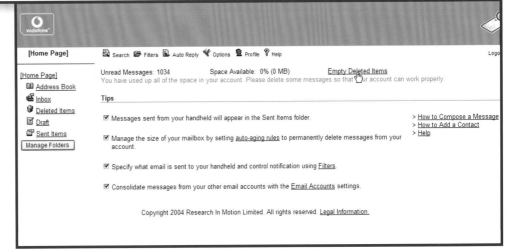

What happens next?

Having thus configured your BlackBerry service, four things happen:

1. The webmail service regularly checks your email accounts for new incoming email.

2. New messages are left on the email server for you to collect manually.

3. A copy of each is transferred to the webmail Inbox and stored there.

4. These messages are then also sent over the GPRS network to the BlackBerry device, whereupon you can read them as you roam.

The second point demands special mention. In Step 6 on p.64, we saw an option to leave messages on the server. The advantage of checking this box is that you can log into your email accounts to retrieve your messages on your desktop system when you return to base, despite having already seen them on the move with your BlackBerry. However, bearing in mind what we said in the Email strategy section on p.56, there is a danger that an email server will hit its Inbox storage limit and start bouncing messages. This puts the onus on you to log in and purge old messages (which, given a GPRS connection, you should actually be able to do from the BlackBerry itself).

You might prefer to leave this box unchecked, in which case the BlackBerry service will move rather than copy all new messages to the webmail folders and your BlackBerry device. You can then synchronise the BlackBerry folders with your desktop email program when you get home. Synchronisation software is supplied.

Either way, here's what a BlackBerry looks like in practice.

When new email is received, the BlackBerry's light glows red and an envelope icon displays the number of unread messages. Select the Messages icon on the main menu with the thumbwheel and press it once to click.

Here we have the message folder where email and text messages are stored. A sealed red envelope denotes a new, unread email. Use the thumbwheel to scroll through the list and click on any message.

Up pops an options menu. Select Open with the thumbwheel and click.

You can now read your email message on the BlackBerry screen. If the message is too long, scroll down with the thumbwheel. Click the thumbwheel again to return to the options menu or use the back button to return to the message folder.

You might, for instance, want to reply to a message. When you select Reply from the options menu, the BlackBerry generates a new email window with the sender's email address already in place in the To: field. Type away.

Now click the thumbwheel again, scroll down to Send and click once. Your email will be sent through the GPRS network to the webmail service and from there to the recipient. It really is as simple as that.

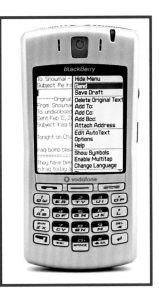

Costs

As we write, the BlackBerry 7100v from Vodafone costs anywhere from zero to £100 depending upon the contract and pricing tariff. For instance, you can pay £100 for the device itself with an £18.50 monthly charge for the email service. You'll be billed separately for telephone calls at 50p per minute. Or you can have the device for half that price if you prefer the Anytime200 scheme. The email charge is reduced to £15 but there's an additional £30 per month to pay for the mobile phone service. But this includes 200 minutes of free phone calls…

Well, you know the routine. There are plenty of options, and none of them are particularly transparent, particularly if you then browse the web over GPRS and incur bandwidth charges. If something like the BlackBerry appeals, take a deep breath and have a chat with your local mobile shop.

Vodafone's current BlackBerry pricing. Whichever way you cut it, a dedicated mobile email service is not cheap, but it is undeniably convenient.

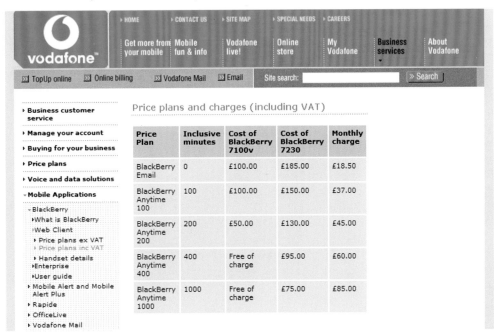

Price plans and charges (including VAT)

Price Plan	Inclusive minutes	Cost of BlackBerry 7100v	Cost of BlackBerry 7230	Monthly charge
BlackBerry Email	0	£100.00	£185.00	£18.50
BlackBerry Anytime 100	100	£100.00	£150.00	£37.00
BlackBerry Anytime 200	200	£50.00	£130.00	£45.00
BlackBerry Anytime 400	400	Free of charge	£95.00	£60.00
BlackBerry Anytime 1000	1000	Free of charge	£75.00	£85.00

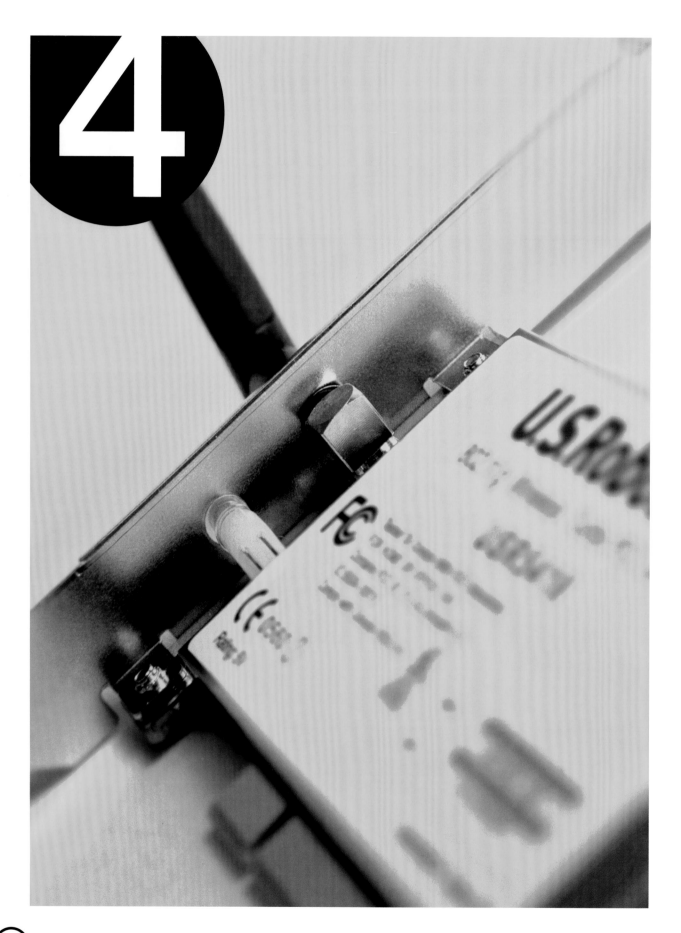

PART 4 Putting theory into practice with a PDA

PART 4 Setting up your PDA

Setting up a Palm PC or Pocket PC isn't difficult, although when you open the box you might be surprised by the number of cables, connectors and other paraphernalia accompanying a so-called pocketable device. For starters, there'll be a USB cable to connect the PDA to the USB port of a desktop PC and a power cable to connect the PDA to its power supply. If you live in the UK, this will be the usual plastic box with three prongs, designed to plug directly into a mains socket.

In most cases (but not with any model in the PalmOne Zire family), there will be a cradle. This acts as a stand for the device when using it in the home or office and also makes it easier to charge your PDA and connect it to your desktop. You simply connect the power supply and USB leads to the cradle instead of to the PDA and then, when you want to charge or connect your PDA, drop it into its cradle. Bear in mind that the cradle supplied with your PDA is not necessarily interchangeable with other models from the same maker. A universal cradle is available for certain models of Pocket PC but in general a cradle is designed to fit the precise shape of the product with which it is supplied.

Other goodies in the box with your PDA might include earphones and miscellaneous connectors, and there will definitely be a rechargeable battery. This may be pre-installed inside the device. Although you'll probably be keen to switch on your new PDA and start using it straight away, you'll have to be patient for a while. First you have to fully charge the battery, which could take several hours. It's not a good idea to use the PDA during its initial charge or to merely part-charge it before trying it out. Doing so can decrease the battery's future storage potential.

On a CD-ROM, you'll find the software that handles the transfer and synchronisation of data between the PDA and the host PC. This program must be installed on the host PC. The CD should also contain optional programs and utilities, some for the PDA and some for the host PC, plus all the key documentation in electronic format. It's unusual to receive comprehensive printed

A PDA in its cradle can synchronise with a desktop PC while simultaneously recharging its internal battery.

Power cords and cables are all part of the PDA package.

manuals with a PDA, even if it's a top-of-the-range model. The best you can hope for are 'Read Me First' and 'Getting Started' guides. Pocket PC buyers will find a comprehensive user guide in Adobe Acrobat format on the CD, but Palm PC buyers are not supplied with a full user guide in either printed or electronic form. Instead, they can access it through PalmOne's web pages. While this means it's always bang up to date, it's far less convenient than having your own copy.

First steps with a Pocket PC

With the battery fully charged you can switch on your Pocket PC and follow the simple on-screen instructions for setting it up. These start with the calibration process, which ensures that when you touch the stylus to the screen the machine knows exactly which part of the screen you are tapping on. All you're required to do is to follow a cross-hair cursor around the screen, clicking when requested, and then make a couple of test selections from dummy menus. Be as accurate as you can at this stage, but if you later find your pointing technique improves you can re-run the calibration process as often as you like.

Once your PDA is up and running, you can install the software from the CD-ROM onto your desktop PC (or laptop), but don't connect the PDA or its cradle to the PC's USB port until you are prompted to do so. The connection software for Pocket PCs is called ActiveSync. If you're using Windows XP with the Service Pack 2 upgrade you'll have to give it permission to work through the Windows firewall. Click 'Unblock' when prompted.

ActiveSync offers two types of partnership: standard or guest. A standard partnership is the norm if you are connecting to your own PC. It's the most intimate relationship and allows data to be synchronised between your PDA and your desktop machine. A guest partnership allows files to be transferred but does not permit data to be synchronised with Microsoft Outlook on the host PC.

As you progress through the ActiveSync wizard you'll get a chance to specify which shared data files, apart from those in Outlook, should be synchronised. There's no need to worry about remembering everything at this stage because you can add files to the synchronisation list at any time.

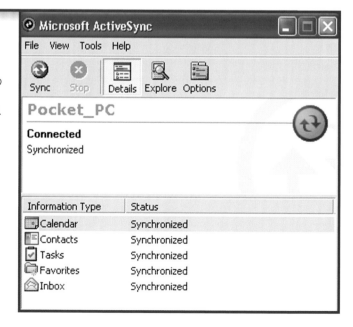

Microsoft ActiveSync copies over to the PDA all the data from your desktop PC that you've asked it to synchronise and then continues to display the ActiveSync Window. This might take several minutes during the initial run because all the data has to be transferred from desktop to PDA. In future, only data which has been changed on either machine will need to be transferred.

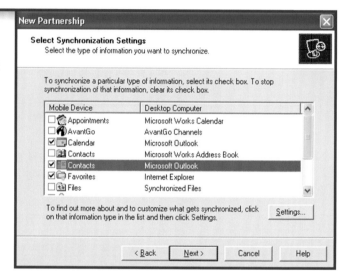

Pocket PC software

Some of the software on the installation CD that ships with a Pocket PC is complete and licensed, but other titles are shareware or trial versions. If you've never used a PDA before, it's a good idea to defer installing any additional programs until you've got a better grasp of the software that's built into the device itself. There's no point in clogging up the limited amount of program storage space with titles you might never need or use.

One of the most popular titles is AvantGo, a program which enables you to download pages from the web and take them with you to read on the road (see p.142–144). Also genuinely useful if you've got a Bluetooth-enabled mobile phone is BVRP's Bluetooth Phone Manager. This guides you through the Pocket PC and phone pairing process, enabling you to connect to the internet while away from your desk using the modem in your phone.

If your Pocket PC is one of HP's Mobile Media devices (rx3700 or similar), you'll find a host of programs designed to make the most of its additional features. For instance, NevoMedia Server enables it to function as a server for music, video and still pictures. NevoBackup is another worthwhile option. Be warned, however, that installing these programs also involves installing Microsoft.NET Framework 1.1 on your PC, which is a major step and perhaps one that's worth postponing until you've got to know your Pocket PC better.

There are many more programs available for download from **www.ipaqchoice.com**. This is a Hewlett Packard site where, as well as downloadable software, you can also choose from a host of accessories. You can even buy a maintenance contract for the care and repair of your iPAQ Pocket PC. Another useful HP site for help with installing and using your PDA is here: **www.hp.com/support**.

NevoMedia makes it possible to view media files on a Pocket PC.

First steps with a Palm PC

Setting up a Palm PC is slightly easier than setting up a Pocket PC because you're not obliged to calibrate the screen first. Should calibration prove necessary in the future you can perform it at any time by choosing Digitizer on the Preferences screen.

Install the Palm Desktop synchronisation software on your PC before connecting the Palm PC or the USB cable. Simply insert the installation CD and follow the onscreen instructions. You'll have to choose a folder on the desktop PC for the Palm Desktop software. Once the program has been installed, restart the PC when prompted.

Next pick a username that identifies your PDA to your desktop PC and choose whether you want to synchronise your PDA data with Palm Desktop or with both Palm Desktop and Microsoft Outlook. If you're already an Outlook user you'll choose the latter, but if you're new to computerised address books, it's less fuss to use the Palm Desktop software.

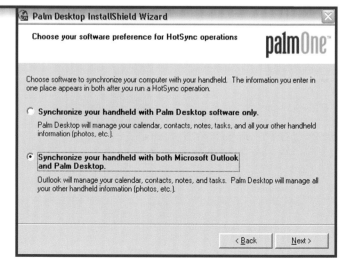

Connect the USB cable and tap the HotSync button on the handheld (either on the main Applications screen or by using the star icon in the user input area). If you've chosen to synchronise with Outlook, this pipes over all your existing contacts, tasks, notes and calendar entries. When this is complete, you can choose to register your PDA with PalmOne in order to receive technical support, or you can proceed straight to the installation of optional software.

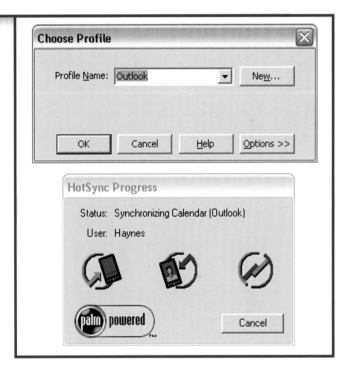

To begin with we suggest you install only three optional items:
- The Getting Started guide, so you can read it on your PDA as well as your PC.
- Versamail, so you can send and receive emails using your PDA.
- Documents to Go, so you can create and edit Word and Excel documents and share them with your PC.

Later you can return to the CD to install additional programs, media players and utilities once you've sorted out your priorities.

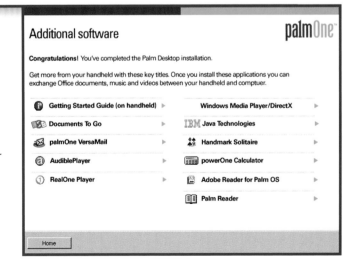

PART ④ Synchronising with a desktop PC

When you first get your PDA, you'll be keen to pipe data into it from your desktop PC and see how the two devices interact.

This means you'll want to get ActiveSync or HotSync Manager up and running as soon as possible. ActiveSync is for Pocket PCs and HotSync Manager is for Palm PCs. Once you've been using your PDA and desktop computer in tandem for some time, you'll doubtless think of ways in which you want to customise the synchronising process to suit the way you work. This is achieved by setting options that determine not only what gets synchronised, but when. There's also the opportunity to dictate which device gets priority when the data stored on them conflicts. This can happen when, for example, a contact phone number has been changed on both machines since the previous synchronisation.

Customising HotSync Manager for Palm PCs

To customise the way that synchronising takes place, click the HotSync Manager icon in the Windows tool tray, and select 'Custom' from the popup menu. To change the synchronisation options for any item, first select the item and then click the 'Change' button. The four options are: synchronise the item so that the most recent version takes priority; do nothing; give priority to the desktop; or give priority to the portable device.

Usually, the synchronise option is best, but there might be occasions when you want to give priority to one device rather than another. An example would be if you had suffered a hard disk crash on the desktop and wanted to reinstate the names in your desktop contacts list by piping them over from the PDA.

For items where the synchronise option is chosen, you might also wish to set a rule that governs which device gets priority in the case of conflicting changes. To do this, click the 'Settings' button and open the drop-down list labelled 'Conflict Resolution'. You can choose either Outlook or the remote device as the automatic winner of any conflict, or you can choose 'Duplicate'. The latter option copies all desktop records to the Palm PC and all Palm PC records to the desktop. There's also an option to ignore conflicts, which does not synchronise them at all but rather allows the conflicting versions to remain in place on their respective machines.

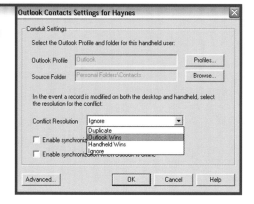

Synchronising a Pocket PC

Start ActiveSync on the host PC by selecting it from the Start menu or, if minimised, by double clicking its icon on the Windows taskbar. Click the Options icon on the toolbar. If the toolbar is not visible, select Options from the Tools menu.

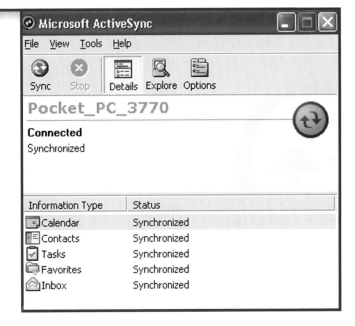

In the central scrolling list, select those items you wish to synchronise by ticking them. You will see that there is an option to synchronise Pocket Access files, yet you'll search in vain to find Pocket Access on your PDA. The reason is that Microsoft discontinued the Pocket Access software back in the days when Pocket PCs were called Handheld PCs. The option is there for compatibility with older equipment and for users who have installed a third party alternative to Pocket Access that uses the same files.

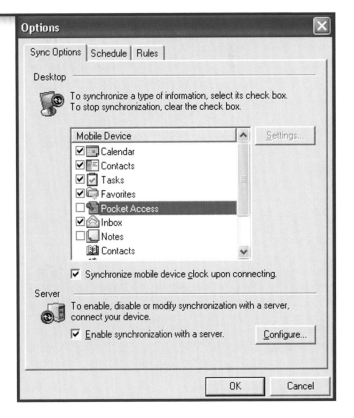

One of the things most Pocket PC users need to do is to synchronise files other than those listed in ActiveSync. These include Word, Excel and text files, as well as data files for any third-party programs you may have added. To synchronise any type of file, tick Files in the ActiveSync list. A message appears telling you that a synchronisation folder will be created on the host PC's hard disk. Click OK.

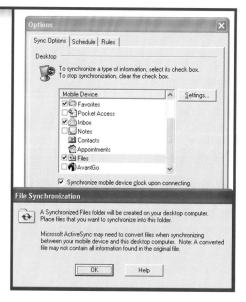

The next time you synchronise, files and folders from My Documents on the Pocket PC will automatically be copied to this new synchronisation folder on the desktop PC. You can copy files from the host PC to the Pocket PC by moving them into this folder.
Note: Once a file has been synchronised, deleting it on either device will cause it to be deleted from the other device during the next synchronisation process. Remember this and copy any files you definitely want to keep into a separate folder before deleting them.

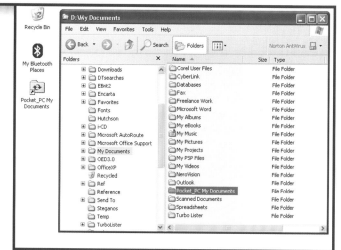

The way in which items are synchronised is controlled by settings that work independently of those chosen for other items. For example, you can choose settings to synchronise your Inbox that have no impact on the settings you choose for Contacts. To see how this works, select Inbox and then click the Settings button. The principal options are how many lines of each email message you want to copy to your Pocket PC, and how many days back you need to go when synchronising. Simply uncheck these options if you want to allow messages of unrestricted length and age. By default, file attachments are not synchronised along with their parent messages but, by changing the settings on this screen, you can choose to include them and set a limit on their permissible sizes. Click OK after making any changes.

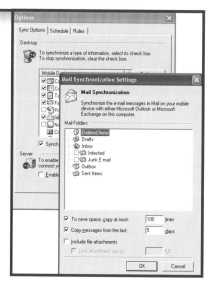

Whereas the Settings button provides control over each synchronised item, the two tabs at the top of the Options dialog box set global preferences. The Schedule tab is where you determine when synchronisation takes place. The frequency of synchronisation can be set independently for connections with a desktop PC or a company network; while for wireless (i.e. Bluetooth) synchronising you can choose a split scheme for peak and off-peak synchronisations. You can even define your own peak times, because not everybody works nine to five.

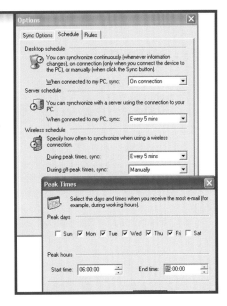

The Rules tab is really two tabs in one, because it's where you choose how version conflicts will be resolved (i.e. when an item has changed on both the desktop and the mobile computer) and how files will be converted when they are passed between the two machines. Use the drop-down Conflict Resolution list to assign priority to the desktop or mobile device, or choose to leave conflicts unresolved so that you can sort them out for yourself. The best option for you will depend on whether you perform the bulk of your data entry on the base machine or on the road.

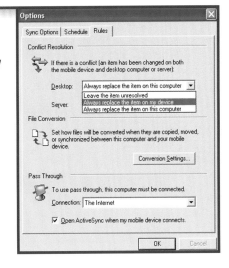

To change file conversion preferences, click the Conversion Settings button. This reveals three additional tabs. On the General tab, you can decide whether to turn conversions on or off. Usually you'll want them on because turning them off may result in some types of file being unreadable on the Pocket PC. On occasions where there is a certain type of file you don't want to be converted (perhaps because you want to transfer it unchanged to a different PC), you can disable conversions for that specific file type on the other two tabs. Simply select the file type you want to modify and then click the Edit button. If you want files to remain unchanged, select 'No conversion' from the drop-down list.

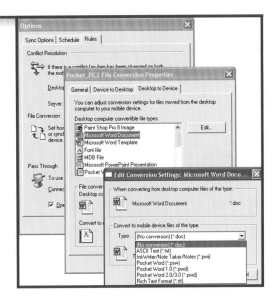

Synchronising a Pocket PC using Bluetooth

The usual way of synchronising a Pocket PC with its host PC is via a USB cable. This requires no additional setting up after installing ActiveSync from the set-up CD, and is also the fastest means of sharing data. However, you may wish to use Bluetooth to carry out a completely wireless synchronisation. One advantage of this is that you can synchronise your machines whenever they are within Bluetooth range (usually 10 metres), so that you are no longer tied to your computer desk by a fixed-length USB cable.

Synchronising via Bluetooth relies on Bluetooth's serial port services, so before you can configure ActiveSync you need to set up the desktop PC for Bluetooth serial communications. If the host computer is a notebook with built-in Bluetooth you'll use the software and drivers provided by its manufacturer; but if you've added Bluetooth by plugging in a USB adapter, you'll use the software provided with the device.

Incidentally, if you're running Windows XP on a desktop PC and you've installed the SP2 upgrade, you might have problems getting Bluetooth to work with a plug-in USB adapter. This is a known glitch: see p.165.

The following step-by-step guide uses a plug-in Belkin Bluetooth adapter in a desktop PC.

1

Double-click the Bluetooth icon on the Windows taskbar to start the Bluetooth configuration utility, or invoke it via Control Panel on the Start menu. View the available Bluetooth services and locate the Bluetooth Serial Port service. Right click this item to set its Properties.

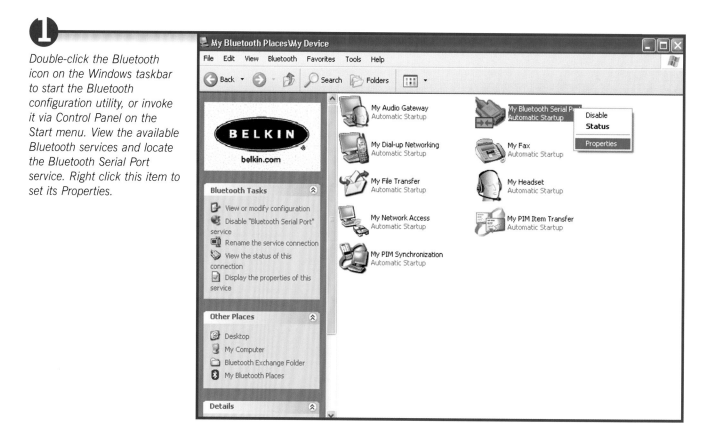

In the Bluetooth Properties dialog box, ensure that the service is set to start automatically and that a COM port number is displayed. Make a note of the COM port number. If you wish to save yourself having to specify a password every time you use ActiveSync, remove the tick from the 'Secure Connection' box. Click OK.

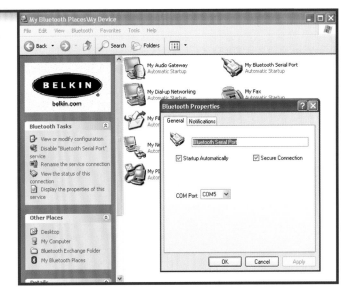

Place your Pocket PC in its cradle or connect it to a USB port so that ActiveSync opens and synchronisation takes place. Open the ActiveSync File menu and click Connection Settings. Make sure that 'Allow serial cable or infrared connection to this COM port' is ticked. Crucially, you must also remove the ticks from 'Allow USB connection...' and 'Allow network...'. Only when you've cleared both these ticks should you click OK.

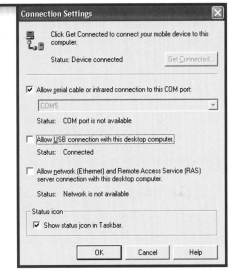

ActiveSync will now display a 'Not connected' message. Click File and Connection Settings to reopen the dialog box you've just been using. You will now be able to change the number of the serial port used by ActiveSync. Make sure it is the same port number you made a note of in Step 2. Click OK to close the dialog box. You may now disconnect your Pocket PC from its USB connection.

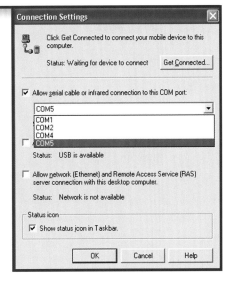

On the Pocket PC opening screen, tap the Wireless Communication or Bluetooth icon in the lower right-hand corner of the screen. Close any Help screens that pop up. If Bluetooth is not already enabled, there will be a white X in a red circle on its button. In this case, click the button to turn Bluetooth on and then tap Manager to start Bluetooth Manager. Tap the Tools menu at the bottom of the screen and select Paired devices.

Tap Add to display the Bluetooth Device Pairing screen, then tap the Search icon (a page with a magnifying glass) to begin looking for new devices. When the name of the host PC you wish to synchronise with is displayed, select it. You must now type a passkey, which can be anything you want. Keep things simple by using just four letters or numbers. Tap OK.

A popup message will appear on the host PC, which you must click to confirm your willingness to connect with the Pocket PC. When prompted, type the same passkey you used on the Pocket PC.

Bluetooth Manager on the Pocket PC now displays the name of the host PC as a paired device. Tap OK. At the bottom of the screen, on the menu bar, you should now see a Bluetooth icon. Tap this to activate the Bluetooth Connection Wizard, then tap 'ActiveSync via Bluetooth'.

On the next two screens, tap Next to proceed. On the third screen, tap the host PC's icon to initiate the Bluetooth discovery process. It should only take a couple of seconds for a connection to be established to the host PC. Once the link has been made you should save it as a shortcut for future use with the suggested name or one of your own choosing.

On the host PC, another pop-up message like the one in Step 7 appears. Click this and your Pocket PC will almost instantly start synchronising using ActiveSync. If you are presented with a Bluetooth Service Authorization dialog box instead, tick to select the option that always allows your Pocket PC to have serial access to the host computer, then click OK.

Once a Bluetooth serial connection has been established and saved as a shortcut, it's very easy to reconnect in future. All that's required is to make sure Bluetooth is turned on and then open Bluetooth Manager. Tap twice in quick succession on the shortcut you saved in Step 9 and the rest is automatic. If you find double-tapping onerous, press and hold the stylus on the shortcut until a context menu appears, then tap Connect.

To switch between USB and Bluetooth synchronisation methods, open the File menu in ActiveSync and select Connection Settings. For Bluetooth, tick 'Allow serial cable or infrared connection to this COM port'; and for USB, tick 'Allow USB connection with this desktop computer'. Even though these selections are not mutually exclusive, you should only select one of them. It may be necessary to restart Windows before the change is recognised.

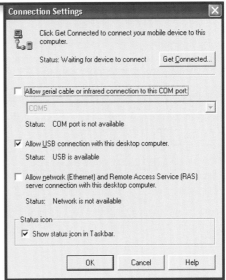

PART 4 Input techniques

The easiest way of getting data into your PDA is to pipe it over from your PC. Even though there are several clever ways of inputting fresh data using only a stylus, they are all likely to be considerably slower than your normal typing speed. This is true even if you're a fumble-fingered typist who can't always remember where the keys are.

Pocket PC input techniques

There are no fewer than four ways of entering text and numbers into a Pocket PC, plus a kind of cheat. Here's a roundup.

Screen keyboard

This is the method that most people use when they're starting out, because it takes no time to learn. Whenever input is required, the onscreen keyboard appears in the lower third of the screen. Letters can be selected by tapping them with the stylus. A so-called 'sticky' Shift key stays down while you type the next character, making it possible to access the full range of keyboard symbols.

How easy you find the keyboard to use depends to a large extent on your eyesight and hand/eye coordination skills. Many people find the virtual keyboard too small, in which case you can enlarge the virtual keys, but this has the disadvantage of showing fewer keys on the screen and forcing you to use Shift more often.

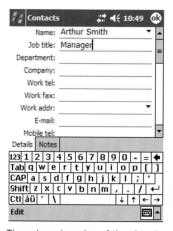

The enlarged version of the virtual keyboard, right, is easier to use but shows fewer symbols.

Block Recognizer

An alternative to the virtual keyboard is the Block Recognizer. This replaces the virtual keyboard with two input areas: one on the left for alphabetic characters and one on the right for numbers and symbols. You create characters by drawing them with the stylus, using an unforgiving system in which some letters are always entered in lower-case form, some in upper case and others as special squiggles. As if this wasn't confusing enough, you have to keep moving the stylus between the left (alphabetic) and right (symbol) sides of the block input area. Fortunately, there's a built-in tutorial to teach you how each character and number is formed.

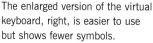
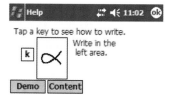

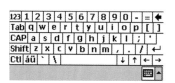

The Block Recognizer tutorial teaches you how to form letters and numbers.

Letter Recognizer

The Letter Recognizer bears certain similarities to the Block Recognizer, but instead of having to learn new ways of forming characters, you use the familiar printing technique that everybody is taught at school. The snag is that the screen input area is even more complicated than for the Block Recognizer. There are three separate entry areas for lower case letters, upper case letters and numbers. Letters are always entered in lower case form, so it's where you enter them that determines whether they will be displayed as capitals. An added complication is that characters with tails must be entered above a dashed line for them to be correctly recognized.

Relive the frustration of learning infant school printing with Letter Recognizer.

Transcriber

This is the most sophisticated input option. Unlike the other three methods, which all involve inputting one character at a time, Transcriber lets you write or print complete phrases and sentences. It is, in fact, a form of handwriting recognition and it works well once you've instructed Transcriber about the way you form your letters. Although Transcriber is a good option for general text input, it's not so good for names and addresses, many of which will be words that do not feature in Transcriber's internal dictionary and are likely to be misinterpreted. There is also a delay of several seconds at the end of every phrase or sentence for translation. Only once a phrase has been cleared from the screen should you continue with the next sentence.

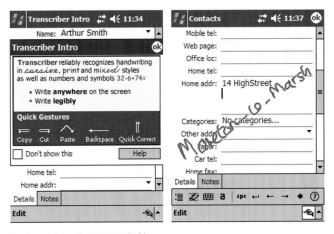

The tutorial for Transcriber (left) teaches you how to make special movements for editing. On the right, you can see Transcriber in action.

Notes

In some situations, such as when using the Pocket PC application called Notes, you can dispense with formal input techniques altogether. Notes lets you treat the screen as a sheet of electronic paper on which you can write or draw as you see fit (like a Tablet PC in miniature, in fact). Note-taking facilities are also incorporated in the Calendar, Contacts and Tasks applications. What you enter on the screen is stored as an image but once a note is finished, it can be turned into text using the Recognize command on the Tool menu. However, if a note includes drawings as well as text, the results can be unpredictable. Notes can also be beamed to another Pocket PC via infrared.

Text and drawings can be combined in a note (left) but, for the purposes of handwriting recognition, it's better not to include pictures (right).

Palm PC input techniques

The Palm operating system doesn't offer as many forms of direct input as Windows on a Pocket PC, but the two systems that can be used – Graffiti and an onscreen keyboard – are very easy to learn and highly effective. Palm PCs also feature a tool called Note Pad, which is similar to the Notes facility of a Pocket PC and enables you to combine text and diagrams by drawing with the stylus.

Graffiti

As originally conceived, and as implemented on early Palm PCs, Graffiti was a stylised language in which each letter and number was represented by a simplified shape that could be made with the stylus. Nowadays, all Palm PCs use Graffiti 2, a much improved input system where virtually all characters and numbers are formed much as they are in ordinary printing. Characters are input not on the touch-sensitive screen but in the user input area below, and according to which part of the input area you use they will be displayed in lower or upper case. Learning Graffiti takes minutes rather than days.

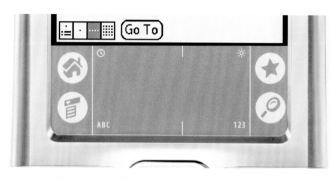

The user input area of a Palm PC. Enter lower case Graffiti characters on the left, numbers on the right and capitals in the middle.

Summon the Graffiti help screen by sliding the stylus up the screen from bottom to top.

Screen keyboard

The alternative to Graffiti is an onscreen keyboard. This can be summoned by tapping the 'ABC' legend in the bottom left of the user input area. Tapping the '123' legend on the right of the input area produces a numeric keypad accompanied by common symbols. There's an international onscreen keyboard too, for occasions when you might need to produce accented characters.

The three guises of the Palm onscreen keyboard.

Beaming business cards

The golden rule of data entry into a PDA is: don't do it at all unless there's no other way! Take the routine exchange of business cards, for instance. Rather than laboriously copying information from a business card onto your PDA with a stylus, leave it until you're sitting at your desktop PC then create a new contact and pipe it over during the synchronisation process. Better still, if the person you're swapping cards with also has a PDA, simply beam your digital cards to each other. It takes seconds.

Business cards can be beamed via infrared or Bluetooth. Beaming between Palm PCs and Pocket PCs is possible, but the process is simpler when each person has the same type of device. For example, to beam business cards between two Palm PCs, simply point them at the each other and press their Contacts buttons.

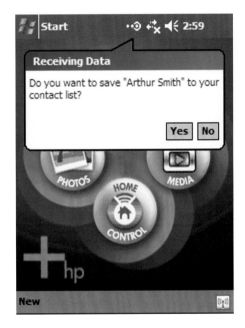

A business card arriving at a Pocket PC when sent from a Palm PC via Bluetooth.

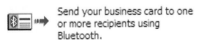

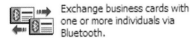

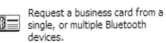

Using the Card Exchange options on a Pocket PC, you can choose whether to send, receive or exchange business cards with one or more devices.

PDA software

Aside from the operating system, three types of program are supplied with every PDA:

- Embedded programs stored in ROM. These can never be erased and will even survive a hard reset that wipes out everything else in memory. ROM programs include the operating system and additional tools such as Word and Excel on a Pocket PC.
- Optional programs supplied on CD-ROM. These can be transferred via the host PC and stored in the PDA's user memory.
- CD-ROM programs designed to run on the host PC rather than the PDA. Two absolutely essential examples are the synchronising programs designed to handle information sharing between the host PC and the PDA. The Pocket PC version is called ActiveSync and the Palm PC version is Palm Desktop.

In this section, we'll look at how to install and uninstall software and glance at some of the most popular applications.

Programs on a Pocket PC can be accessed from a Start menu not too different from the one used in desktop Windows.

Office assistants

The operating system hard-wired into every new Pocket PC (at the time of writing) is Windows Mobile 2003. However, every mobile version of Windows, going right back to early efforts such as Windows CE, comes with a similar set of supporting programs including 'pocket' versions of Excel and Word.

While it's nice to see names that are familiar to many users from their desktop PCs, it's a mistake to think they are the same programs. Excel files from a desktop PC cannot simply be loaded into the PDA version of Excel, edited and then sent back to the desktop. When you transfer an Excel file from your desktop to your PDA it is converted into Pocket Excel format. This causes it to lose many of its features, including drawings, cell notes, text boxes, embedded objects and conditional formatting. If you try to beat the system by opening an Excel document on your PDA without first converting it, there's a catch: all the unviewable items that are normally stripped out of Pocket Excel files will be preserved but they'll later be stripped out if you attempt to save any changes to the file.

Word is similarly restricted – you can't use tables, headers or footers, for example – but the missing features seem to matter less when word processing. As with Excel, you can load and read any document produced by the desktop version of the program, but don't save the document if you'll ever need to use it again on a desktop PC.

Word and Excel are perfectly useable on a Pocket PC, but many users soon decide that programs specifically designed for use on PDAs with small touch-sensitive screens are preferable to cut-down heavyweight contenders.

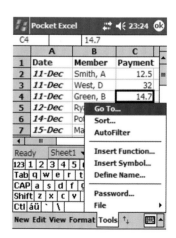

Pocket Excel can look pretty cramped if used with an onscreen keyboard and drop-down menus.

Using MS Office documents on a Palm PC

Palm PCs don't have native support for Microsoft Office documents built into them. However, you will find an amazing program called Documents To Go on the installation CD. Once this is installed on your Palm PC, you can download Word and Excel documents to your portable device where you can read or edit them. If you also choose to have the documents synchronised, any changes you make to the documents on your PDA will be reflected on your desktop PC during the next synchronisation. Unlike Word and Excel on a Pocket PC, Documents To Go allows you to change a document on your PDA without overwriting its format.

The Standard version of Documents To Go comes free with Palm PCs. By upgrading to the Professional edition, you can also use PowerPoint presentations on your Palm PC. The Premium version adds support for spell checking, graphics, PDF files and much more.

A Documents To Go utility program is installed on the host PC. Using this you can choose which Word and Excel files are to be synchronised with your Palm PC.

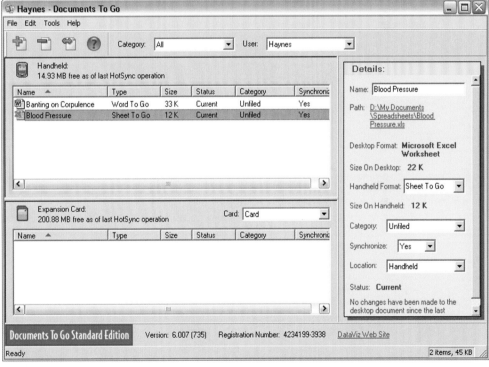

An Excel spreadsheet viewed in Documents To Go.

There are three levels of zoom for Word files in Documents To Go. The smallest size shows the full page width but is too small for editing. This is the intermediate size.

Installing and removing programs on a Pocket PC

Programs for Pocket PCs must be installed before you can use them: they won't work if you simply copy them to your Pocket PC's internal memory store. This is because programs are distributed as Windows applications, so you must first run them on the host PC and then let Windows pipe them over to the Pocket PC using ActiveSync.

The usual way of obtaining programs is to download them from the web, but some programs, particularly commercial offerings, are supplied on CD-ROM. You'll find a selection of full and trial software on the disc that comes with your Pocket PC.

When you wish to remove a program from your Pocket PC, you should not simply delete its files from the internal memory store. This will leave inactive links and Start menu entries, and basically break things. You should instead use one of the methods described below to remove not only the program file but all its links, icons and menu entries.

If a program is supplied or downloaded in compressed (zipped) format, you'll have to extract its contents first. With your Pocket PC installed in its cradle or connected to a USB port, fire up Windows Explorer on your desktop PC and navigate to the program you wish to install. Double-click the executable program file to begin installing it. After the usual preamble about licensing agreements you'll be asked if you want the program installed in the default program folder of your Pocket PC. In most cases, you click Yes to agree to this.

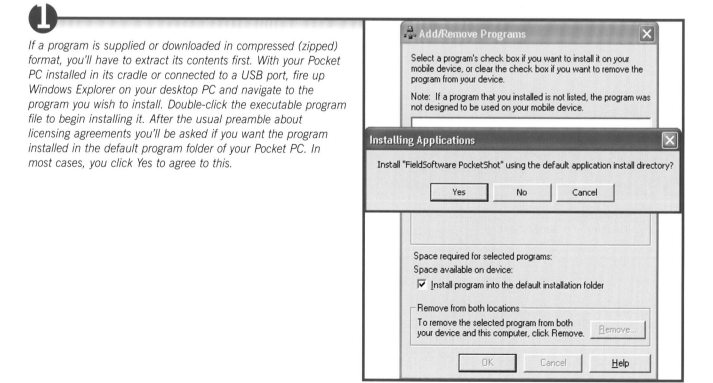

The program is then transferred and a message is displayed on the host PC telling you to check the handheld device to see if any further installation steps are necessary. If the Pocket PC displays a message that the program may not work properly because it was designed for a previous version of Windows, simply click OK. Most older programs will run perfectly on newer machines (though you may have problems if you try to install the latest programs on older Pocket PCs).

A program can be uninstalled (deleted) by running its install program for a second time, and then clicking 'No' in Step 1. This displays an Add/Remove programs dialog box on the desktop PC. Simply remove the tick from the check box of the program you wish to uninstall and click OK.

Another method of uninstalling a program from a Pocket PC has the advantage of working even when the portable device is not linked to its host PC. Open the Pocket PC menu and tap Settings. Then select the System tab and tap Remove Programs. Every program installed on the machine is listed. Select the one you wish to uninstall and tap Remove.

Installing and removing programs on a Palm PC

Major programs for the Palm PC come with their own set-up routines which ensure that the appropriate files are piped over to your Palm PC via the HotSync process. Programs you download from the web usually consist of a single file with the extension .PRC. Once this file has been unzipped into a folder on your PC's hard disk, it is transferred to the PDA during the next HotSync of data.

HotSync cannot be expected to know that there is a program to be installed unless you tell it so, which is where the PalmOne Quick Install utility comes in. You'll find this program in the Palm Desktop group on the Windows Start button. When it is running, two panels are displayed, one representing the main memory of your Palm PC and the other representing the expansion card. To install a program you simply drag its .PRC file into the appropriate panel, and then tap the HotSync button on your PDA.

To remove a program you no longer need from a Palm PC, display the Applications screen and open the menu by tapping the tab at the top of the screen. Tap Delete to view a list of all the installed programs. Select the program you wish to remove and then tap the Delete button. Once you confirm your decision, the job is done.

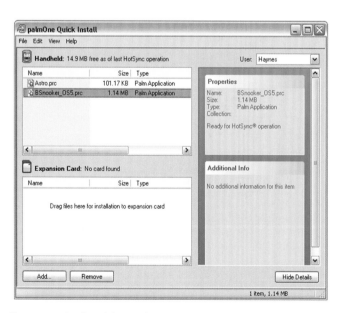

Accessing the Delete application command from the Applications screen of a Palm PC (left) and selecting a specific program for deletion (right).

If you are not a fan of drag and drop, click the Add button in the Quick Install Window and you can browse for the files to be installed.

Where to find additional software ...

For many PDA owners, every program they'll ever use is either built into their device or provided on its installation CD-ROM. But for a truly huge choice of practical, utility and entertainment software you can turn to third-party software developers, many of whom specialise in producing software for PDAs.

Nearly all PDA programs are sold by direct download, so you can pay for them by credit card and be using them within minutes of deciding to purchase. In addition to commercial software, there are plenty of free programs and shareware programs out there. Rather than track down suppliers individually, visit the websites of specialist PDA software libraries. Here you will find commercial software sitting alongside freeware and shareware titles.

A one-stop source for Palm PC programs is **www.palmgear.com**, where you can choose from over 26,000 titles. The equivalent site for Pocket PC users is **www.pocketgear.com**. Another incredibly useful link is **www.pdastreet.com**. This is a network of sites devoted to PDAs of all types, not only Pocket PCs and Palm PCs but also BlackBerrys, smartphones and obsolete devices from Psion, Apple, HP and others.

Once you're familiar with your PDA, it's worth going back to its installation CD to see what might have passed you by when you were eager to get started.

More than 5000 of the titles available at **www.palmgear.com** are free.

From the PDA Street main menu you can jump to a number of specialist sites for news, forums, advice and reviews, as well as software downloads.

And what to do with it

Control domestic appliances with an iPAQ 3715.

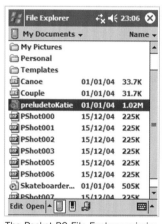

Play videos with Pocket PC Mobile Media Player.

Pocket PC Calculator.

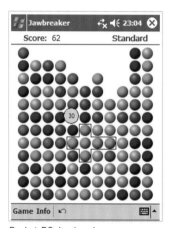

Pocket PC Jawbreaker game.

Slideshow picture viewer on HP iPAQ.

The Pocket PC File Explorer mimics Windows Explorer on a PC.

Pocket Excel running on an iPAQ.

Pocket PC Task Manager.

Web pages can look mighty cramped on Pocket Internet Explorer.

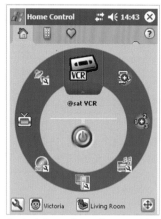

AvantGo offline web pages (seen here on a Pocket PC) can be viewed on any type of PDA.

The email inbox of a Pocket PC.

Editing a Word file on a Palm PC using Documents To Go.

Viewing three different world times on a Palm PC.

Recording a voice memo on a Palm PC.

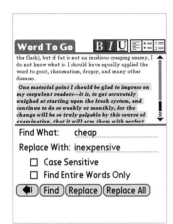

Palm Reader lets you carry complete books around with you.

Note Pad on the Palm PC is similar to Notes on the Pocket PC.

Palm PCs have a dedicated program for logging expenses.

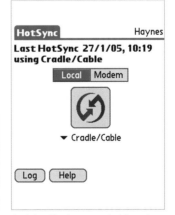

The contact list on a Palm PC can be synchronised with Outlook or Palm Desktop.

The Palm Calendar program is also an appointments diary.

Just tap the large central icon to perform an automatic HotSync with a desktop PC.

PART  # Internet telephony

PART 5 Introducing VoIP

The mobile phone has become such an everyday commodity that we now take it for granted that we can be reached wherever we go. Even when we travel abroad, it is usually possible to enable network 'roaming' in order to make and take calls. All of this is fine when somebody else is paying the bills, of course, but the costs of making international calls on a mobile phone can be horrendous.

Cue VoIP, or Voice over Internet protocol, or internet telephony, or whatever you want to call it. The principle is simple: why use a landline or mobile telephone to make calls if you have access to the internet? Given that you'll be paying for the internet connection already, one way or another, any calls you make will effectively be free. The trick is knowing how to make an internet telephone call.

How it works

When you make a call through the internet with a VoIP service, the sound of your voice is turned into a highly-compressed digital stream, broken into a series of discrete data 'packets', and fired off through your internet connection. At the other end of the call, these packets are stitched back together into the digital signal and converted back into sound. When it works well, it's transparent and seamless.

Now, it has to be said that VoIP is not a perfect technology. For one thing, the quality of internet telephone calls is limited by the available bandwidth. This is commonly thought of as the *speed* of the connection – a broadband connection is 'faster' than a dial-up connection – but it's more accurate to think in terms of how much data can be transferred from point to point per second. It comes to much the same thing, in fact: a broadband connection can handle at least 10 times more data per second than a dial-up connection. Because a high-quality digital sound signal requires a good deal of bandwidth, broadband is better suited to VoIP. To help things along, VoIP systems also use compression to reduce the quantity of raw data required to digitally encode the sound of your voice.

Even with a broadband internet connection at either end of an internet call, things can go wrong. If the stream of data does not arrive as quickly as it is sent, the odd packet can get dropped here and there. This leads to a characteristic stuttering in VoIP calls where words occasionally get cut in half or syllables disappear. The problem is compounded when callers talk over one another. Calls sent over the public internet are also vulnerable to the effects of interference, 'noise' on the line, bottlenecks and general internet traffic.

All of this being said, it is perhaps surprising that VoIP works at all. But work it does.

The principle of VoIP is making telephone calls over a broadband internet connection.

Choices for voices

There are in fact three different models of VoIP:

● At the simplest level, you can call another computer from your own computer. Both parties must be online at the same time and using the same software for this to work, but calls are free so you can talk to somebody on the other side of the world without any time limit.

● The next step is a computer-to-telephone service whereby you can make outgoing calls from your computer to normal landline and mobile numbers. This is usually considerably cheaper than using the phone, particularly when calling from overseas.

● Finally, there's an emerging breed of VoIP services which let you make and, crucially, *receive* calls on a standard telephone connected to the internet. You even get a new phone number as part of the deal.

Hardware requirements vary according to the type of VoIP service you use. For computer-to-computer or computer-to-phone calls, you must, of course, have a computer. To be heard, you should connect a microphone to the appropriate socket on the computer's sound card; and to hear your callers, you can either use computer speakers or, preferably, headphones. A headset with a built-in microphone is a better bet by far. USB models generally offer superior quality and some even have their own audio circuitry built-in (which means your computer needn't have a sound card at all). Headsets also avoid the problem of whistle-and-wail feedback. Better still is a plug-in USB handset that looks and feels like a normal mobile phone. Cordless (Wi-Fi) models are also on their way.

Get yourself a fold-up, portable USB headset for high-quality VoIP calls.

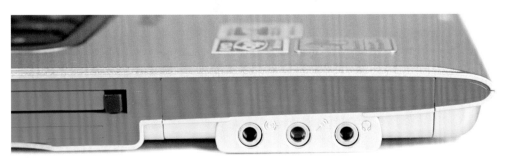

Virtually all laptops have sound ports for connecting microphones and headphones.

VoIP on the move

The benefits of VoIP to the traveller are significant. It's likely that VoIP services will become readily available in internet cafés and hotspots around the world, but this is also a technology that you can take with you. So long as you can establish an internet connection and run the appropriate software on a compatible device, you can make free calls. Skype, for instance, is available on Pocket PCs and SoftPhone (p.114) provides outgoing and incoming VoIP calls on a laptop. What's more, although VoIP works best on broadband, you can use these service over a dial-up internet connection.

Key points to bear in mind are:

- Any VoIP service benefits from as much free bandwidth as possible. This means that if you pick up email, surf the web or do anything else whatsoever on the internet during a call, the quality will suffer. You may even lose the call completely. If you have a home network with internet sharing, be sure that Junior isn't downloading MP3s in the next room while you're calling Australia.
- It may take a moment or two for the words you speak to reach the listener and vice versa. Think of a transatlantic telephone call with a slight time delay. Get used to waiting a couple of seconds to make sure that the other party has finished before you reply. Try not to talk over one another.
- Internet connections are often protected by a firewall, as indeed they should be. If you find that you can't make a connection, have a word with whoever is in charge of your company network. If the buck stops with you, you may have to open a port or two on your router to allow calls in and out. However, Skype, the VoIP service that we'll be looking at in detail here, claims to work around most standard firewall configurations. We've certainly tested it in a variety of domestic and commercial settings without difficulty.

Free telephone calls from a Pocket PC with Skype.

PART  Computer-to-computer calls

Here, we will work through the procedure for setting up and using Skype, an innovative but straightforward VoIP service. Once you have this up and running on a laptop or a Wi-Fi-enabled Pocket PC, you can call any of your Skype contacts from wherever you have an internet connection, anywhere in the world. This includes wireless hotspots in coffee shops and airports and broadband lines in hotel bedrooms.

Even if you don't have broadband on hand – for instance, if you find yourself stuck in a hotel room with only a telephone line – all is not lost. Hook up your hardware via a dial-up connection to a local ISP (see p.60) and you can call home or anywhere else for the price of a local call. The quality may not be brilliant but it should be acceptable and will cost very much less than using a mobile phone or making an international call.

We'll work with the PC version here but Skype is also available for Mac and Linux.

*Skype is available as a free download from **www.skype.com**. The system requirements are fairly onerous – your laptop should have a 400MHz processor, 128MB of RAM and Windows 2000 or XP – plus you'll need a sound card, microphone and speakers or a USB headset. Download the file to your desktop and double-click it to run the installation procedure.*

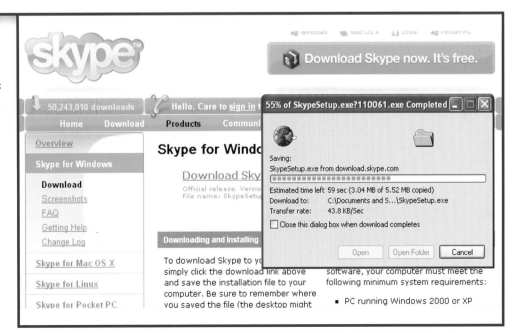

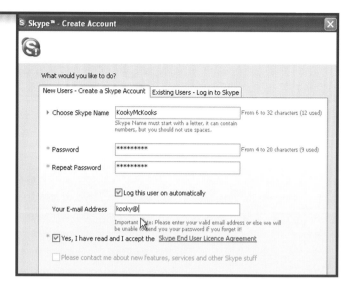

The tricky part of registration is picking a user name that is not already in use (at the time of writing, Skype claims over 90 million downloads). You don't have to use your real name. Put a tick in the 'Log this user on automatically' box to save having to enter your user name and password in the future.

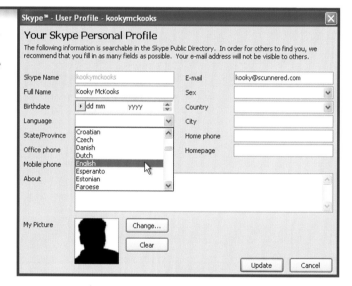

Next up is an optional profile page which reflects how others see you. Be warned that anything you put here, including your telephone number, can be seen by other Skype users. Telephone numbers will become important later (see p.108–112). You can leave your profile entirely blank if you prefer.

You can change the picture shown in your profile. Click Select to access one of the tacky Skype themes or click Add to select an alternative picture on your computer (JPG or BMP file formats only). If you have a picture of yourself, so much the better.

Skype now launches in a window and looks thoroughly unpromising. The problem is that you have nobody to talk to, so the next stage is getting a contact to sign up for Skype. Click the 'Share Skype with a Friend' link to send an introductory email. We'll assume that this friend joins the Skype service and tells you their user name. Now you must buddy up.

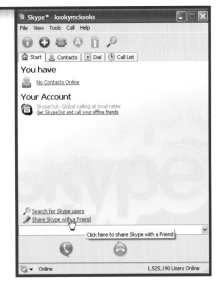

Click 'Search for Skype users'. Up pops a search window. You can now search for your friend's Skype name or, if you click the Advanced button, their real name (assuming they entered this truthfully in the profile page seen in Step 3). You can also search for a known email address.

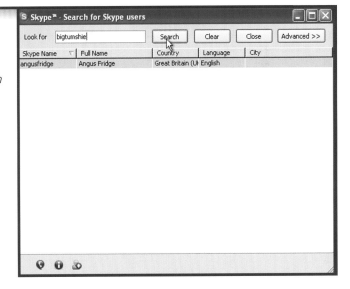

When Skype locates your friend, click the Add to Contacts button at the bottom of the screen (or right-click your friend's name and select Add to Contacts).

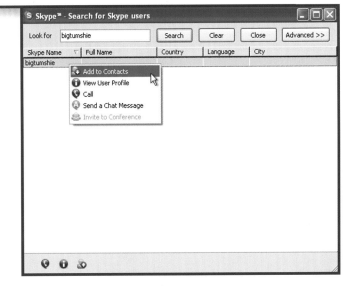

Skype now automatically generates a message to send to your friend. The default setting is the one you want here, as it allows both parties to see when the other is online (something that's essential for voice chat, as we shall see). Click OK.

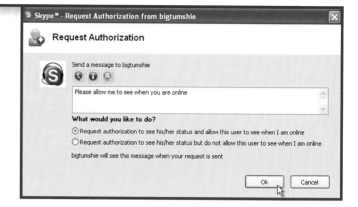

If your friend is currently online and signed in to Skype, they will receive your message. They can then accept you as a contact or block you from ever getting in touch again. If they are not online or signed in, they will receive your invitation when they next use Skype. Only one of you needs to initiate this contact-making: so long as the other party accepts the invitation, buddying-up is automatic and reciprocal.

Let's now work through a voice call from scratch. Here, playing the part of 'kookymckooks', we can see that one contact is online. Open the Contacts tab for details.

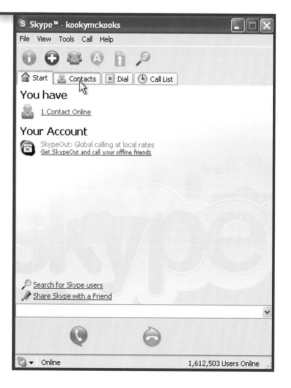

'Bigtumshie' appears in the Contacts window. The green icon confirms that he's online, so kookymckooks can initiate a call. However, we'll assume that he wants to check first whether bigtumshie is happy to chat. Right-click the contact name and select Start Chat.

This fires up a text chat window which will be familiar to you if you've ever used an instant messenger. Type a message in the lower part of the window and hit the Return key to send it (or click the Return-style button). Your message pops up on the other party's screen.

Like this. 'Bigtumshie' can now type a reply. At any time, either party can click the green telephone icon in the main toolbar or under the contact's name to start a voice call.

If you don't want to bother with text chat, simply highlight your contact in the Contact tab and click the big green telephone button at the bottom of the window. You'll hear a ringing sound as Skype tries to make the connection.

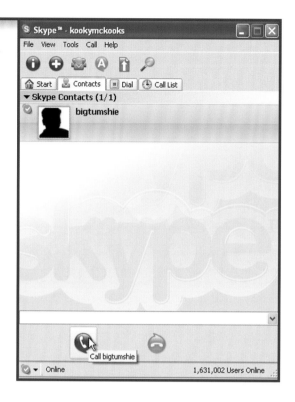

An incoming call window now pops up on bigtumshie's screen. When he clicks his own green telephone button, the two parties can chat as if in a telephone conversation. There are no time limits and no costs. At any point, either party can click the red button to end the call.

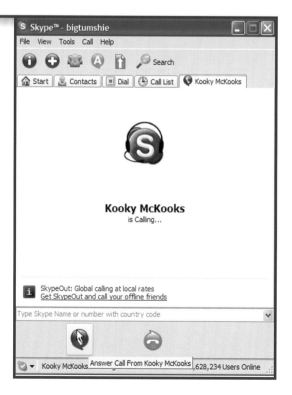

When the call concludes, open the Call List to see a summary. In this case, the call between kookymckooks and bigtumshie lasted 1 minute and 37 seconds and took place today. The four icons let you sort the call log in terms of all calls (grey), missed calls (red), incoming calls (green) and outgoing calls (blue). The dropdown field further lets you sort calls by contact name. The bin icon clears the log.

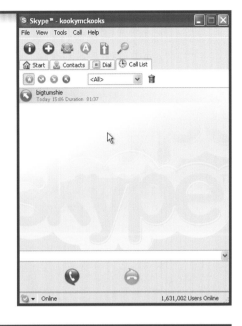

If you want to leave Skype running but don't want to take any calls, click File, Change Status and select Do Not Disturb. This mutes any incoming ringing sounds. Alternatively, if you want real peace and quiet, change your status to Offline. Nobody can now call you (and nor can you make calls out).

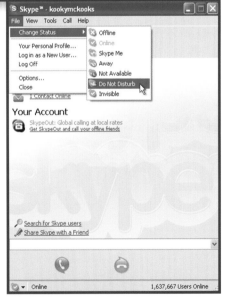

Surprisingly, the File > Close command merely minimises Skype to an icon in the taskbar, as does clicking the standard program close button in the main window. If you want to close Skype completely right-click the taskbar icon and select Quit. You can also change your status with a right-click here.

PART

Computer-to-telephone calls

Calling other computers over the internet is one thing but calling a real telephone number is something else entirely. We're going to stick with Skype here and use its SkypeOut feature. This goes well beyond computer-to-computer calls and lets you call any landline or mobile number in the world (well, nearly) at a reasonable rate. If you've tried the likes of Callserve (**www.callserve.com**) or Net2Phone (**www.net2phone.com**), you'll know the idea. For our money, though, SkypeOut is easier to use and offers significantly superior call quality.

You can call all of these countries for a flat-rate of 1.7 Euro cents per minute (correct at time of writing):

Argentina	France	Norway
Australia	Germany	Portugal
Austria	Ireland	Russia
Belgium	Italy	Spain
Canada	Mexico	Sweden
Chile	Netherlands	United Kingdom
Denmark	New Zealand	United States

SykpeOut offers simplified global pricing.

Calls to UK mobile telephone numbers cost just over 2 cents per minute and calls to Samoa reach the giddy heights of 3 cents. Remember, these charges apply from anywhere in the world, which means you can call a UK number for 1.7 cents per minute from Land's End, Liechtenstein or Little Rock, Arkansas. Full details can be found on the Skype website (**www.skype.com**).

Note that all of these rates are subject to 15% VAT, the Luxembourg rate which Skype charges throughout Europe. Call charges are also rounded up to the nearest minute, not charged by the second, so a call lasting 1 minute and 10 seconds is billed as a 2 minute call. Calls to some premium rate numbers – and, crucially, to the emergency services – are not possible.

*First, you need to set up a Skype account as described earlier. Now pay a visit to the Skype website (***www.skype.com***) and follow the link to buy credit. With SkypeOut, you buy credit upfront and then use it as and when you like. You'll be asked to sign in with your Skype user name and password.*

Sign in or create new account

- **You need to sign in with your Skype Name to continue.**

You need to sign in with your existing Skype Name and password or new users can create an account and get a Skype Name. Creating an account and getting a Skype Name is free.

Sign in

I am already using Skype and I would like to sign in:

Skype Name
kookymckooks

Password
****
Forgot your password?

Sign me in

Complete the registration form. While Skype doesn't care what user name or profile you use, or indeed whether you specified your real name in Step 2 on p.10, you do have to supply your real name and address here. You'll be prompted to provide credit card details too. Note that VAT is applied at the rate of 15%. Payment made, Skype ties the credit balance to your account.

Skype Order 2583646

Description	Amount
SkypeOut calling worth of 10 Euros	€ 10.00
Subtotal	€ 10.00
15% LUX VAT (Who must pay this?)	€ 1.50
Total (this amount will be charged to you)	€ 11.50

If you would like to cancel your order, simply close this browser window or click Cancel Order.

Your payment will be handled by Bibit Global Payments Services. The name Skype or Internet address www.skype.com may appear on your bank statement.

You can only make use of the SkypeOut calling service when your account has a positive and sufficient credit balance. Charges shall be calculated by multiplying the duration of the call by the applicable tariff. The duration of a call shall be based on one-minute increments and fractions of minutes will be rounded up. During the call, charges incurred will be deducted automatically from your account.

Payment for this order means acceptance with Skype's Terms of Service.

Payment Details

Payment reference number	2583646
Amount to pay	EUR 11.50
Payment with	Visa

You can now use Skype to call telephone numbers. To do so, open the Dial tab in the main program window and enter a number using either the onscreen dialpad or your keyboard. You must enter the full international code even if you're calling a UK number from the UK (remember, Skype doesn't know or care where you are physically located). Press the green telephone button (or hit return) to make the call. Use the red button to hang up.

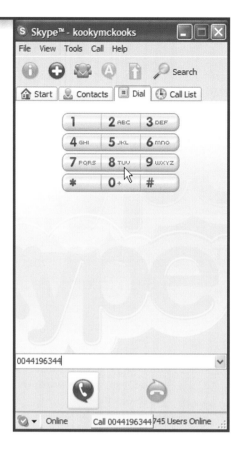

During a call, click anywhere in the window to access menu options that let you mute the call or put it on hold. Click again to see the same menu and reverse your earlier action. For instance, during a SkypeOut call, you can put the current call on hold and initiate a second call.

You can also accept incoming calls from Skype contacts during a SkypeOut call, in which case Skype will prompt you to put the SkypeOut call on hold. When you have two (or more) calls in progress simultaneously, Skype provides a tab for each. Switch between these to put calls on or off hold.

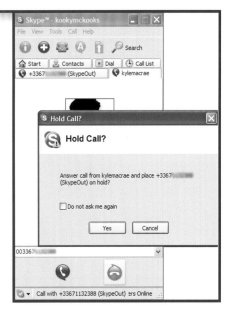

To view your remaining call credit, click Tools then Go to My Account Page. Log in to the Skype site when prompted and you'll see your balance. You can also access your call history here, download invoices for credit already purchased, and buy more credit as and when required. If you don't make a call for 180 days, any credit balance is lost.

Open the Call List tab to see numbers that you have dialled previously. You can click on a number here and then click the green telephone button to save having to re-enter it, like a last number redial feature. You can also use the drop-down telephone number field at the bottom of the window for this.

Right-click a previously dialled number in your Call List and select Add to Contacts. This adds the telephone number to your address book. Give it a name, click Next and click Finish. You can also add SkypeOut contacts manually by clicking Tools and Add a Contact.

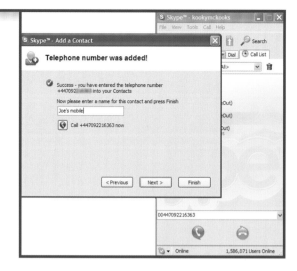

In your Contacts tab, you will now find a second category called SkypeOut. Contacts have a different style of icon. To initiate a telephone call to a SkypeOut contact, select their name and click the green telephone button.

When a Skype user includes telephone numbers in their personal profile (see Step 3 on p.102), these appear in the contacts pane. Click directly on a telephone number here to call it with SkypeOut. You can, of course, do this even when the contact is offline and thus unavailable to take a Skype computer-to-computer call.

PART

INTERNET TELEPHONY

Full-blown VoIP

SkypeOut is undeniably useful but there are two significant drawbacks. The first is that you can only make calls when your computer is turned on and connected to the internet, even if you use a USB handset. The second is that you can not *receive* telephone calls from landline or mobile numbers. Inbound calls can come only from Skype contacts on a computer-to-computer basis. There are plans to offer an inbound service called SkypeIn but at the time of writing it had not been launched. What we need is a VoIP system that offers full two-way integration with the standard telephone network.

Plug and go

There are various ways to achieve inbound VoIP but the usual model involves a telephone adapter that either sits between the internet connection and the computer or that connects to a router. This lets you connect a standard telephone to the adapter and make calls over the internet. In order to *receive* calls you do, of course, need a telephone number on which people can call you. This is provided by the adapter. In other words, you gain a second telephone line. This all works entirely independently of your computer, which need not be turned on or connected in any way. Indeed, you don't need a computer at all.

The system is entirely portable at the technical level, which means you can use it anywhere. For instance, you could take your adapter to the far side of the world, plug it into a broadband line, connect a handset and make and receive calls on your new, personal telephone number. Because this is VoIP technology, your geographical location doesn't matter at all. Calls cost just the same from Honolulu as from home.

A simple VoIP configuration where a telephone adapter enables you to make internet calls with any standard telephone.

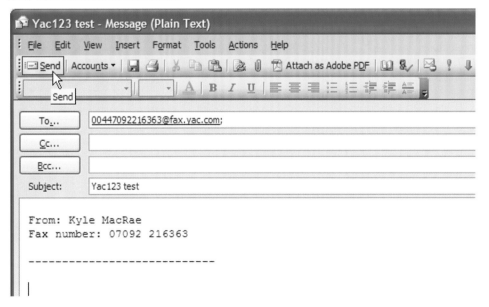

A Vonage telephone adapter provides a personal, portable VoIP telephone number. One for the hand luggage.

VoIP-ing with Vonage

The most recent and arguably the most innovative VoIP service to launch in the UK is from Vonage (**www.vonage.co.uk**). The running costs are bound to change but as we write there's a fixed fee of £9.99 per month. This includes unlimited free calls to UK and Eire landlines. Calls to UK mobiles cost 5p, 10p or 15p per minute, depending on the time of the call, and international calls range from 2p per minute (to Canada, Hong Kong and parts of Europe) through to £2.28 per minute (Tuvalu).

At the launch, all UK personal numbers begin with 020 – i.e. a London code – but regional variations are promised. For instance, if you live in Liverpool, it should be possible to select a personal number with a Liverpool dialling code. This means that your neighbours can call you at local rates rather than paying national rate to call London.

Just to be clear, anybody calling your Vonage number will pay the same local or national rate regardless of where you happen to be in the world at the time. The same applies to calls you make. For instance, you can call any UK landline from a Sydney Harbour café for as long as you like for absolutely no call cost – so long as your telephone adapter is connected to the internet via broadband.

It's all very clever and means that you can, in effect, take a relatively cheap telephone number with you when you travel. If only you didn't have to lug around a telephone adapter and handset…

SoftPhone

In fact, Vonage has that covered with its add-on SoftPhone feature (currently priced at £5.99 per month). This is a software-only application that effectively mimics the hardware telephone adapter and lets you make VoIP calls with a headset or USB phone connected to a laptop. This means that you could, for instance, connect your laptop to the internet in a Wi-Fi hotspot, pop on your headset and make (and receive) free or cheap telephone calls. Voicemail, message forwarding and a separate portable fax number come as standard.

If you're feeling really optimistic, we understand that you can even install SoftPhone on a Wi-Fi-enabled Pocket PC, thereby turning it into a truly mobile, wireless VoIP handset. We haven't had the chance to test this but check out this web page for a guide: **www.engadget.com/entry/6437880577833191**.

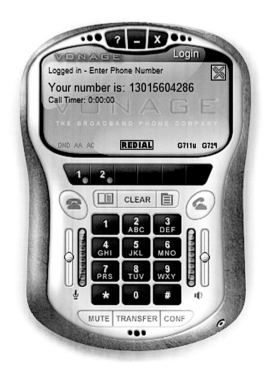

SoftPhone lets you make and take telephone calls on your laptop wherever you find a broadband internet connection.

PART

A telephone number that follows you anywhere

You know the problem: you have a home number, a work number, a fax number, a mobile number and now, quite conceivably, a VoIP number. You can never remember them all so little wonder if nobody else can. Wouldn't it be nice if you only had one number that you could take with you anywhere? Wouldn't it be convenient for all concerned if somebody calling this number was automatically diverted to whichever telephone you happen to be near at the time – be it in a hotel room or an office, a friend's number, your mobile phone, your VoIP service or whatever – whether at home or abroad? Sometimes you may not want to be contacted, in which case a voicemail service would be handy – and how much handier still if those messages were forwarded to you as email. A fax facility might also be useful, especially if you could receive *and* send faxes without needing a fax machine.

Ah, the simple life: one number on your business card, email signature and other contact details, no matter how much you travel.

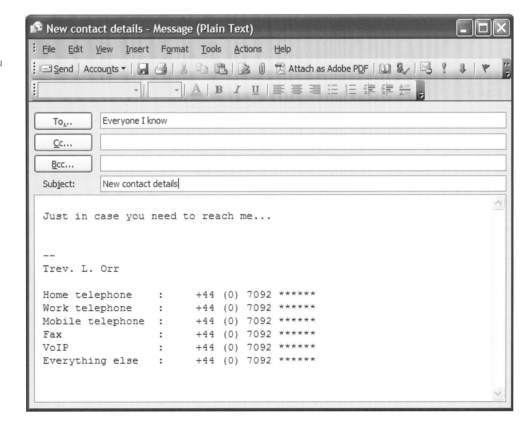

These are some of the benefits of a 'unified personal number'. In principle, it's the only number you need ever give out to anybody you meet. Here, we'll get one from Yac (**www.yac.com**).

Before getting too excited, there's one significant drawback that we should mention at the outset. When you sign up with Yac, you are allocated a premium-rate 'personal' 0709 number. These numbers are very expensive indeed to call. In the UK, for instance, a call to a Yac number from a BT landline currently costs 37.5p per minute at peak time, 25p in the evenings and 12.5p at weekends. Business colleagues may shoulder the cost if it means they can track you down anywhere in the world without having to remember a dozen or more numbers but your friends and family will not thank you to be lumbered with such charges for the privilege of calling you at home.

Also note that you can't make calls *out* with a Yac number in the way that you can with SkypeOut, Vonage or any other VoIP service. Think of this primarily as a way to be reached while you travel.

There are currently two main Yac services: Yac Number Basic, which is free; and Yac Number Professional, which costs £35.25 per year. Here are the key differences:

	Yac Number Basic	Yac Number Professional
Call forwarding	Incoming calls can be forwarded to any UK landline. For instance, if you're going to be working in a factory out of town for the day, you can route your Yac number to the factory's switchboard. Callers will then be transferred to that switchboard automatically when they call your Yac number. When you return, you can redirect your Yac number elsewhere or turn off call forwarding altogether.	Incoming calls can be redirected to any UK landline, UK mobile or a landline in any of 100 countries. You can even redirect calls to international mobile numbers, although the Help menu is coy on this point. Note that if you redirect calls to a UK mobile phone and then take it abroad, you will be billed for 'roaming' charges by your mobile network every time you take a call.
Hunting	Call forwarding to two numbers. If the first number goes unanswered, the call is routed to the next number before eventually being diverted to voicemail.	Call forwarding to five numbers. If the first number is unanswered, the call is routed to up to four other numbers before eventually being diverted to voicemail.
Voicemail-to-email	When a caller leaves a message, Yac turns it into a sound file and sends it to your email address as an attachment.	See Yac Number Basic.
Voice message store	As an alternative to email forwarding, Yac will store voicemail messages. You can listen to these messages from any phone simply by dialling your Yac number.	See Yac Number Basic. Additionally, Yac will send a text message to your mobile phone every time a new voicemail message is left.
Fax-to-email	When a caller sends a fax to your Yac number from a fax machine, it is converted to an image file or a PDF file (your choice) and forwarded as an email attachment.	See Yac Number Basic.
Email-to-fax	Unavailable.	Send a fax to any real fax machine in the world using only email. How? See p.118–123.
Caller greeting	Standard ('Press 1 to leave a message; press 2 to send a fax …')	Customisable ('Hi, it's me!')

A Yac number follows you anywhere, home or away.

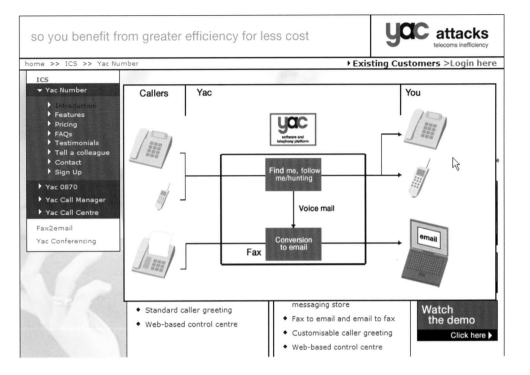

so you benefit from greater efficiency for less cost

yac attacks
telecoms inefficiency

home >> ICS >> Yac Number

▸ **Existing Customers** >Login here

ICS
▾ Yac Number
  ▸ Introduction
  ▸ Features
  ▸ Pricing
  ▸ FAQs
  ▸ Testimonials
  ▸ Tell a colleague
  ▸ Contact
  ▸ Sign Up
▸ Yac 0870
▸ Yac Call Manager
▸ Yac Call Centre

Fax2email
Yac Conferencing

Callers   Yac   You

Find me, follow me/hunting

Voice mail

Conversion to email

Fax

messaging store

• Standard caller greeting
• Web-based control centre

• Fax to email and email to fax
• Customisable caller greeting
• Web-based control centre

Watch the demo
Click here ▸

Tell Yac which numbers you can be reached on and it will hunt you down around the world or, failing that, divert calls to voicemail and forward messages and faxes as email attachments.

Yac Number
▸ Introduction
▸ Features
▸ Pricing
▸ FAQs
▸ Testimonials
▸ Tell a colleague
▸ Contact
▸ Signup

Fax2email
Yac Conferencing

YAC Number Call Forwarding

Your Call Forwarding Settings determine how YAC routes your incoming phone calls.

Just list the numbers at which you most frequently take calls, then select the phone number(s) at which YAC should try to contact you. But don't forget to make sure that Call Forwarding is turned ON. If it is turned OFF, all calls to your YAC Number™ will be sent to your email inbox.

Note: You must enter at least one number to use Call Forwarding.

07092216363
Settings

Main Menu
Call Forwarding / Messaging Options
Voice/Fax Mode
Personal Details
Message Distribution
Number Call Screening
Name Call Screening
Email To Fax
Call History
Personalised Greetings
Help
Support
Logout

1. Your Call Forwarding Numbers
Fill in your Call Forwarding preferences as directed. You must have at least one number filled in to enable the Call Forwarding option.

UK Numbers: [area code]+[number] e.g. 0207 8493507
International: 00+[country code]+[area code]+[number] e.g. 001 408 5557092

Phone Numbers:

Ring Timer

WORK	00▓▓▓▓▓▓▓▓▓	40
MOBILE	00▓▓▓▓▓▓▓	40
HOME	00▓▓▓▓▓▓▓	40
TEMPORARY	00▓▓▓▓▓▓▓	40
2nd TEMPORARY	00▓▓▓▓▓▓▓	40
3rd TEMPORARY		0
4th TEMPORARY		0

2. Your Call Forwarding Options
Select the phone number to which you wish your YAC Number to forward your calls. YAC will call you at each of these numbers in the order of your preference.

1st **Number to call:** TEMPORARY ▾
2nd **Number to call:** MOBILE ▾
3rd **Number to call:** (NONE) ▾
4th **Number to call:** (NONE) ▾
5th **Number to call:** (NONE) ▾

PART

And a virtual fax machine

Fax just won't die. It's a slow, limited and clunky means of communication in an electronic age yet still it finds a place in many businesses. For instance, you may well feel obliged to offer a fax number just to fit in with the antiquated working practices of others ('I have to fax you the paperwork before we can send out the goods').

However, as we have already seen a Yac number fulfils that particular need. Incoming faxes sent to a Yac number are forwarded to you as email attachments. But what about a fax out facility? Just occasionally, you may need to send a fax ('Sign it and fax it back, please') but not, we suspect, often enough to justify buying a dedicated fax machine. Then there's all that palaver of connecting it to the telephone line and stocking it with pape; and as for the mobile worker ... well, fax is simply not a portable technology. Or is it?

Email-to-fax

With a Yac Professional number, you get an email-to-fax service as well as fax-to-email. This means that you can send faxes via email as well as receive them. Indeed, you can send a fax to any fax machine anywhere in the world from any computer that has an internet connection, using either a regular email account or a webmail service like Gmail. You can even fax from a connected PDA, smartphone or BlackBerry. We'll work through the basics in a moment.

First, a word on the pricing. Yac's email-to-fax service requires you to buy credit up front which funds your faxing. The actual pricing is a little obtuse, however, based on how many pages you send and what kind of numbers you call.

Here are some examples – one credit is one penny:

UK fax number called	Credits per page
0800	5
01 / 02 / 0845 / 0870	9
0871	15
070	40 or 50
International fax number called	**Credits per page**
Europe and US	9
Australia	15
India	20
Egypt	30

Sending a fax

When your account is in credit, you can send a fax as easily as sending an email. Simply type your message in the body of the email or attach a document (supported file types include Microsoft Word and Excel, plain and rich text, PDF, HTML, TIF, JPG and GIF). The trouble is that it's not always obvious how many pages you are sending until you get Yac's delivery report. Here's a quick run-through of the procedure, with a couple of tips on how to keep the costs down.

Sign in to Yac, click the Email To Fax link on the control centre page and buy yourself some credit. The minimum purchase is 1000 credits, or £10, for which you'll need a credit card. Remember, you also need to subscribe to the £35/year full-blown Yac Number to use this feature.

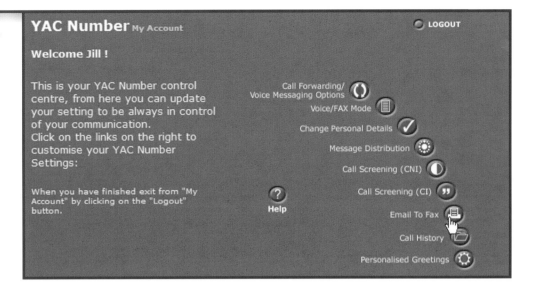

On the Email To Fax page, click Password. We strongly recommend that you create a Yac-only password here rather than using an existing password, especially one that controls access to your bank account or similar. You'll see why in a moment. You don't have to use the same password that you use to log in to Yac itself.

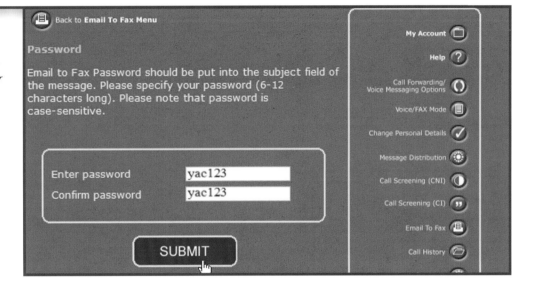

Next, click the Email Address link on the Email To Fax page and specify one or two email addresses that you intend to use. The point is that a fax will only go through if Yac can verify that it was sent from one of these addresses. We suggest making one of these a Gmail (or similar) web-based account that you can access from anywhere, not just from your desktop or laptop computer.

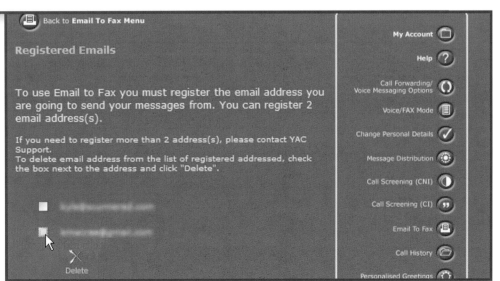

Now click Cover Page. We suggest that you deselect the cover page option here on the basis that you pay per page sent. Why pay a 9p premium to send your contact information as a cover page when you can just as easily incorporate your name and return fax number in the fax itself? We'll show you how shortly (and see Step 7).

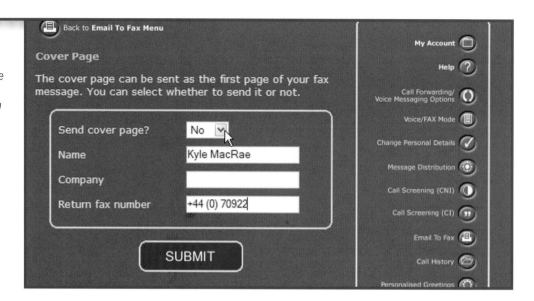

*Time for a test. Open your email program or webmail page and enter your own Yac number (with full international code) in the To field using this format: **number@fax.yac.com**. In the subject field, enter your password from Step 2, followed by a space, and then by anything you like. For the purposes of illustration, we registered the password yac123. Email is inherently insecure so this password could potentially be seen by anyone, which is why we advise using a unique password for Yac's email-to-fax. Type a short message or your return number and send the email.*

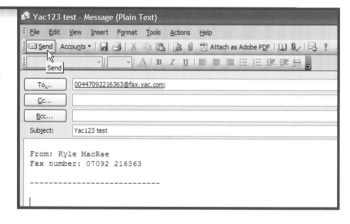

You should shortly receive a Yac delivery status report via email. In this case, our fax failed. Why? Because our email program (Outlook) automatically capitalises the first letter of the Subject field and this has the unfortunate side-effect of changing the first letter of our password from lower to upper case i.e. from yac123 to Yac123. Yac thus rejected the password and the email. So tip number one: use a password that begins either with a number or with a capital letter (or manually edit the Subject field before you click Send).

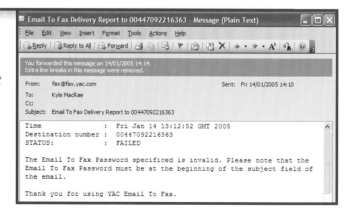

Success. Yac has processed the outbound email and sent the fax message. Because we sent it to a Yac number rather than to a real fax machine, it arrives as an email attachment. You can choose which file format Yac uses for incoming email attachments. We have opted for PDF, but see Step 12. Note what happens if you don't turn off the cover page option in Step 4: even the simplest fax becomes two pages. The second page is merely the body of the email so it's just as easy and half the price to use that space for your contact details.

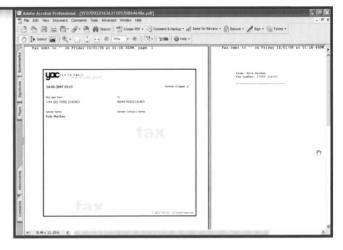

This time, we have turned off the cover sheet option. By switching our email format from plain text to HTML, we can enter a large-font dummy fax header within the body of the email. Note that this time we have also de-capitalised the first letter of the password in the Subject field. Click Send.

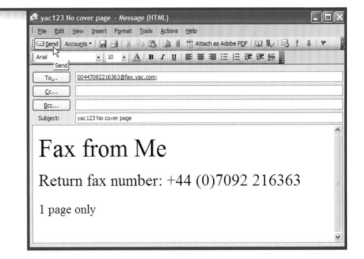

And here it is: a perfectly sufficient one-page fax with a built-in header and plenty of room left for typing the body of a message. Now, none of this is made evident in the Yac guide, in which you include your message as an email attachment. This, of course, means faxing multiple pages which, of course, means more money for Yac. But in many, perhaps most cases, you can get away with sending a simple fax like this.

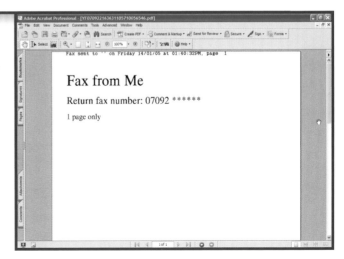

Here's a one-page fax to prove the point. If you use your email program in HTML (or rich text) mode, you can even paste pictures directly into the body of the message. Only if the length of the message exceeds one A4 printed page will you be billed for a second page.

However, you can send attachments if you like, in which case Yac will convert them into printable fax pages. Just attach the file as you would to a normal email and let Yac do the work. Each attachment will be delivered as a separate page or pages.

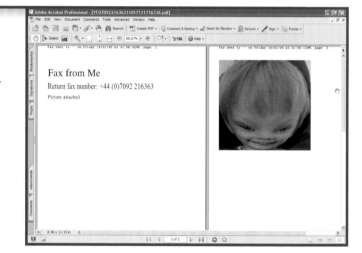

If you're not entirely happy with the appearance of incoming faxes – i.e. faxes that are sent to your Yac number – change the delivery method. This option is rather bizarrely accessed via the Personal Details button on the main Yac Control Centre page. Click this and then click Change Fax File Format. Make a choice between TIFF (an image format) and PDF (a document format) and click Submit. Note that you'll need a copy of Adobe Acrobat Reader to read PDFs. This can be downloaded free of charge from **www.adobe.com/reader**. *If you intend to pick up faxes on a PDA or an internet kiosk, it's safer to select the image format.*

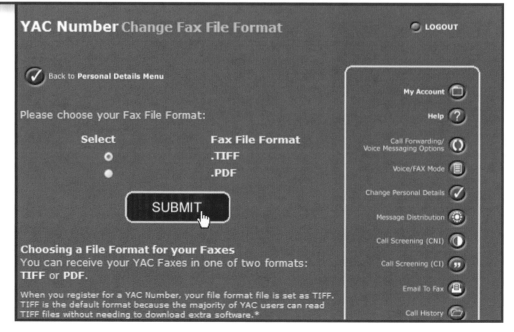

Back on the Yac Email To Fax page, click Message History to access a log of all faxes sent. You can also keep tabs on your expenditure and credit balance. Faxes to other Yac numbers cost a whopping 40p per page, which is faintly ludicrous.

YAC Number Email To Fax · ⟳ **LOGOUT**

▢ Back to **Message History Menu**

Message History Report

Status	Time	From	Destination	Number of Pages	Credits Used
Message discarded	14/01/05 13:05:44	kyle@scunnered.com	07092216363	0	0
Message discarded	14/01/05 13:12:52	kyle@scunnered.com	07092216363	0	0
Success	14/01/05 13:15:56	kyle@scunnered.com	07092216363	2	80
Success	14/01/05 13:25:21	kyle@scunnered.com	07092216363	2	80
Success	14/01/05 13:35:44	kyle@scunnered.com	07092216363	2	80
Success	14/01/05 13:40:05	kyle@scunnered.com	07092216363	1	40
Success	14/01/05 13:46:24	kyle@scunnered.com	07092216363	1	120
Success	14/01/05 13:55:16	kyle@scunnered.com	07092216363	2	160
Success	14/01/05 13:59:05	kmacrae@gmail.com	07092216363	1	120

Two final points. First, if you register a web-based email account with Yac (see Step 3), you can send faxes from anywhere in the world so long as you have access to a web browser. Just remember the **number@fax.yac.com** *and enter your password as the first item in the subject line. You will only pay the standard rate (9p per page) to send a fax to a UK fax number no matter where you send it from.*

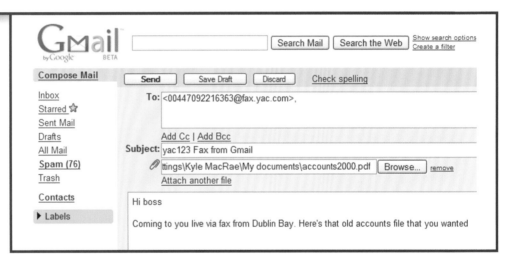

Gmail by Google BETA — [Search Mail] [Search the Web] Show search options / Create a filter

Compose Mail
[Send] [Save Draft] [Discard] Check spelling
Inbox
Starred ☆
Sent Mail   **To:** <00447092216363@fax.yac.com>,
Drafts
All Mail   Add Cc | Add Bcc
Spam (76)   **Subject:** yac123 Fax from Gmail
Trash   📎 ttings\Kyle MacRae\My documents\accounts2000.pdf [Browse...] remove
Contacts   Attach another file
▶ Labels
                 Hi boss

                 Coming to you live via fax from Dublin Bay. Here's that old accounts file that you wanted

Secondly, if you tell Yac to forward incoming faxes to a webmail account, you can access your faxes from any internet-connected computer or device. Click Personal Details on the Yac Control Centre page, then Change Email Address, and specify a Gmail or similar address. Note that voicemail messages will also be delivered to this email address if you have voicemail forwarding turned on.

YAC Voice Message from 05511435768 - 5 Seconds Inbox

☆ **messaging@yac.com** to me

Received: 11:16 on Sat 15/01/05

To listen to your YAC Voice Message, click on the attached file.

YAC CUSTOMER SUPPORT
Contact mailto:help@yac.com or 07092 00 1000.

YAC - You're Always Connected
http://www.yac.com

♬ **yv07092216363110057877881062.wav**
8K Download

Reply Forward Invite messaging@yac.com to Gmail

PART 6

MOBILE TECHNOLOGY MANUAL

GPS: the road warrior's ally

PART  # GPS explained (roughly)

Global Positioning System (GPS) is another buzzword for 2005. Although the technology and the ability to access it has been around for years, the change has evolved through that familiar chicken-and-egg equation of demand and pricing. When the perceived demand for a product or service is high, several suppliers are tempted to enter the market. This introduces competition, which drives down prices. Mass production also reduces the manufacturing costs which in turn means cheaper gadgets in the shops.

Right now, people are taking to GPS with enthusiasm and the technology is finally becoming mainstream. So, three obvious questions:
- What is GPS?
- What can it do for me?
- How do I get it?

Stellar concerns

The Global Positioning System is a constellation of 24 satellites (plus a few spares) each of which orbits the earth twice daily. From any point on earth with a clear view to the sky, at least four satellites are always visible – not to the naked eye but to a GPS receiver. This is a device that picks up radio signals from the satellites and works out how far away each is by analysing the time a signal takes to travel. The longer the signal takes, the further away the satellite. Because the position of each satellite relative to the earth is known precisely, the receiver can plot its own position by analysing the intersections between three or, preferably, four satellite signals.

In two-dimensional terms, it's easy to visualise:
- *Figure 1*: Suppose a subject knows that he is 10km from point A, where point A is a known position. This effectively puts him somewhere – in fact, *anywhere* – on the circumference of a circle radiating from point A. He now has some inkling of his position but not a terribly useful one.
- *Figure 2*: Now introduce another known position, point B, and tell the subject that he is 5km distant. It thus easy to deduce that the subject's position lies at the intersection between the radial circles around points A and B. Trouble is, there are two such intersections.
- *Figure 3*: So we need a third point, C, the position and distance of which from the subject are also known. We now have three radiating circles with only one point of intersection. Here lies, or stands, the subject.

In space, these circles are three-dimensional spheres radiating from satellites, which rather complicates matters. However, the principle is the same. With four satellite positions and distances, or three at a pinch, it is possible to pinpoint your position on the face of Planet Earth. That's the purpose of a GPS receiver.

Figure 1

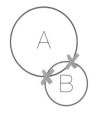

Figure 2

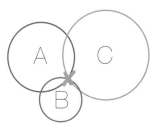

Figure 3

Plotting an amphibious landing zone with GPS. Not, perhaps, a common weekend pastime for most of us.

Bizarrely enough, GPS technology is owned and operated by the US military – it's useful for guiding missiles, among other things – but it's freely available to anybody armed with a GPS receiver. True, the military can turn it off any time they please but this, we trust, is unlikely outside of war zones.

It boils down to this: if you have a GPS receiver and a clearish view of the sky, you can discover your latitude, longitude and altitude to within an accuracy of metres. By itself, of course, this information is merely a bunch of co-ordinates. What you need is a map on which to plot these co-ordinates. This is where GPS becomes useful.

The point of GPS

At the very simplest level, a GPS receiver provides you with sufficient information to plot your position on an Ordnance Survey map. But these days it is virtually a given that the receiver will include its own electronic map and actually show you where you are. Better, it will keep track of you as you travel, which means you can watch yourself – or rather an icon – moving around the map. So long as the sky remains visible and the receiver can 'see' the satellites, you'll know where you are.

This opens some intriguing possibilities. Let's say you're out for a walk in the country, sensibly equipped with a compass and a detailed paper map of the area. You step off the track for a while and suddenly find yourself lost. Obviously, you're only lost in a seemingly trivial and local sense, for you know roughly where you are and, thanks to the compass, in which direction you are heading. The trick is finding some reference point in the surrounding scenery that relates to the map: if that hill to your left is actually this hill shown on the map and that wood behind you is this smudge of green, then you must be here.

Which is great – when the weather is fine, it's daylight and the map is accurate. But it's no use whatsoever when you can't see a single feature of the scenery or make any meaningful relation between what's out there and what's on the map (familiar territory to those of us who can't read a map to save ourselves, perhaps literally). With a GPS receiver, you can plot your precise co-ordinates on the map or, preferably, see your position displayed on a built-in electronic map. In short, you know exactly where you are, day or night. And when you move, you'll still know where you are.

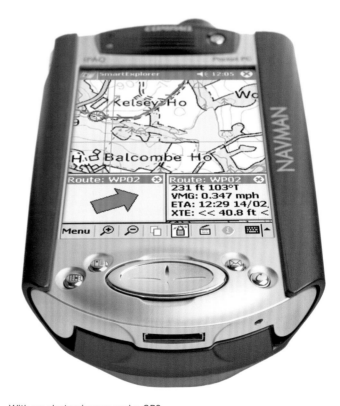

With an electronic map and a GPS receiver in a handheld device, you need never be lost again.

Route planning

If you've used the likes of Microsoft AutoRoute on a computer, you'll know what we mean by route-planning software. You tell a program your starting point, your ultimate destination and where, if anywhere, you want to stop *en route*. With a click of a button, you get full driving instructions with a map and turn-by-turn directions. These you can either memorise or print and take on your travels.

Route-planning with a GPS system can go two steps further. First, it tracks your progress on an electronic map in real time as you travel and, secondly, it tells you when to turn left or right before you reach the junction. If you make a wrong turn or override the instructions, the software will spot this and either invite you to turn around or immediately re-plot a new route from your current position. With everything integrated in a portable device, you can dispense with paper maps altogether.

On foot or on a bike, GPS is a hoot; in a car, it's fantastic. Many cars now have GPS – also called satellite navigation or simply satnav – built in and we're confident that this will soon become a standard fitting. However, you can also install your own in-car GPS kit, as we see on p.133–135.

One other development to watch is the gradual introduction of Assisted GPS (AGPS). The trick is that the GPS receiver passes its raw satellite data to an external server for analysis, using a GPRS network link (see p.47). The resultant location information is then fed back to the receiver in the same way. Shorn of the

In-car satnav used to be the preserve of the posh but not for much longer.

need to perform complex calculations, the receiver can operate significantly faster and carry less hardware, making it lighter and cheaper. It also means that manufacturers can embed satellite navigation in handheld devices that already have network connections. In other words, GPS is coming to smartphones.

It's important not to overstate the benefits of electronic route-planning, even with GPS. No map data is perfect – for instance, the 2005 release of AutoRoute makes no mention of the M6 toll motorway, which opened in 2003, and it suggests a truly bizarre 2700km, four-day trip spanning several countries and taking in a North Sea ferry crossing to get from one Norwegian city to another. Only the most foolhardy driver would trust a business trip or holiday entirely to a computer. You may find yourself disappearing off the edge of a map if you cross an international border or see yourself apparently veering off the road into a neighbouring field or lake should the GPS receiver temporarily lose track of a satellite or two. So-called 'urban canyons' – narrow streets flanked with high buildings – are notoriously problematic for GPS. Some specially coated front windscreens can also effectively block or distort GPS signals, in which case an external receiver is the best or only option. And ultimately there's just no substitute for local knowledge.

It's also all too easy to be distracted by a dashboard-mounted screen and the stream of verbal instructions. One driver reportedly followed GPS instructions to 'perform a U-turn' without hesitation and, you guessed, caused an accident.

However, once tried, forever smitten.

Not the most obvious route from A to B. Don't expect too much from route-planning software.

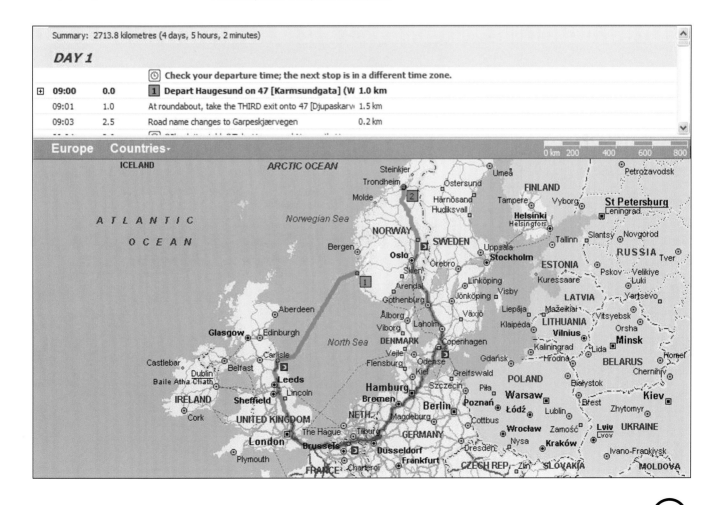

PART **6**

How to buy

GPS receivers come in many guises these days, with an inevitable crossover in functions. However, the two main categories are handheld and in-car devices.

A lightweight handheld GPS device is well suited to rambling, hiking, cycling and 'geocaching' (the obscure but allegedly rewarding sport of using a GPS receiver to seek out secreted caches of 'treasure' hidden around the country: see **www.geocaching.com** and **www.geocacheuk.com** for all you need to know). You can get dedicated GPS devices that do nothing else, GPS receivers that double-up as PDAs, or PDAs with built-in or bolt-on GPS functionality. If you're in the market for a PDA and you travel frequently, we'd suggest that GPS is well worth considering. A PDA with a car adapter – basically a sucker mount for the windscreen – is a particularly attractive option.

If you regularly rack up the miles on unfamiliar routes in your car, whether at home or abroad, a portable in-car GPS unit is a real asset. Just be sure that it comes with maps that cover the areas you'll visit. Most GPS devices are sold only with maps for the region of sale, although you can buy further maps at reasonable cost and easily install them in the device (usually by synchronisation with your computer or on a memory card).

In-car systems tend to be heavier and more robust than true handhelds and can be powered directly from the car battery via the cigarette lighter. You can expect loud verbal directions and a high-visibility screen that is visible in broad daylight. You can also expect to have your GPS unit rapidly stolen if you leave it in place when the car is unattended.

Here's a quick look at a few current models.

Take to the hills with a GPS receiver and follow the clues to uncover hidden treasure.

A GPS-equipped PDA can be used normally when not required for direction finding.

The Garmin iQue 3600 is a Palm OS PDA with a built-in GPS receiver and software.

Everything you need in a box with the TomTom HP Navigation Pack.

The Mitac 168 is a Pocket PC with a built-in GPS receiver.

PDAs

Using a PDA for satellite navigation makes sense because a PDA is small enough to attach to a car dashboard or windscreen with a special cradle. The screen is bright enough to display a map of your current position; and, with an audio-equipped PDA, it is possible to listen to spoken directions.

Pretty much any PDA can be used with a separate external GPS receiver. The receiver then communicates with the PDA via Bluetooth or can be plugged into the PDA's serial link port. However, most PDAs will require a memory upgrade – i.e. a plug-in memory card – in order to store the mapping data for even a single country.

Two of the big names in GPS are Navman and TomTom. For instance, in the UK it is possible to buy a complete kit that includes a Zire 72 PDA, a GPS Bluetooth receiver, car accessories, MapSonic voice navigation software and ViaMichelin map data supplied on its own 128MB SD memory card. Similar packages are available for other countries with different map packages.

TomTom also markets a PDA-plus-GPS-receiver-in-a-box product called TomTom HP Navigation Pack. The bundled HP iPAQ is not top end but it's a neat, semi-integrated approach. If you already own a PDA, you can buy GPS hardware and software separately.

The popular but relatively long-in-the-tooth Mio 168 from Mitac is basically a customised Pocket PC with a built-in, flip-out GPS receiver. It comes with a car adapter kit for temporary dashboard mounting but is light enough to be carried in a pocket and used on foot. The Garmin iQue range serves a similar purpose.

By contrast, the newer Mio 268 scraps all pretence of being a Pocket PC and is quite simply a dedicated handheld GPS device. As with the 168, the receiver is an integral component, not an accessory. It ships with maps for the region in which it is sold and speaks that language, so if you buy one in the UK, driving instructions are in English. If you travel overseas, additional maps can be obtained and installed.

The Mio 269 is virtually identical except that it has an internal 2.5GB hard disk drive. This provides ample storage space for maps that cover 22 European countries, all of which are pre-installed as standard. This is the obvious choice for the overseas traveller. The device will also talk to you in any of nine languages. Both the 268 and 269 can easily be mounted in a car.

But will people settle for a GPS device that doesn't do Word or email, that doesn't function as a telephone, and that doesn't play videos? We rather like this step aside from convergence but time, or rather you, the potential purchaser, will tell.

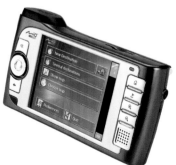

A GPS kit from PalmOne complete with Bluetooth receiver, car mounting kit, power adapters and software.

Take to unfamiliar roads with confidence courtesy of a stick-on GPS unit.

Tell your GPS device – a Mio 269 in this case – where you want to go and it will, or should, get you there.

TomTom Mobile GPS on a Nokia 6600 smartphone.

Much the same thing with the CoPilot Live system.

Smartphones

Given that a smartphone already combines PDA functionality with that of a mobile telephone, why not throw GPS into the mix? True, the screen might be a tad small for easy reference, especially while driving, and the phone's loudspeaker may be found wanting in a horn-blaring capital city traffic jam but the extension is natural and appealing. Take the CoPilot Live Smartphone. This converts a Bluetooth-enabled smartphone running the Microsoft Windows Mobile operating system into a fully-functional GPS receiver. Compatible phones include the Orange SPV C500 and the Motorola MPX 220. Maps and software are supplied on a memory card. The GPS receiver itself is a separate battery-powered unit that communicates with the phone via wireless Bluetooth.

Or take TomTom Mobile, a similar approach that uses different software but takes advantage of a smartphone's Bluetooth connection (models include the Nokia 6600 and Orange SPV E200). For a subscription, you can also get a live traffic information service and thus, in theory, route around hold-ups.

You can also expect to see smartphones with integrated GPS receivers on the market this year. The HP Mobile Messenger on p.41 looks likely to fit the bill but it hasn't been released, or even confirmed, as we write. True, there are clearly technical questions of whether a tiny integrated receiver that doesn't necessarily point skywards will work at all and marketing issues about weight and styling to contend with, but the inexorable trend towards convergence guarantees (or at least very nearly guarantees) that GPS smartphones will hit the shelves soon.

In-car navigation

As discussed above, PDA-style GPS devices can usually be used in the car and are often supplied with some kind of mounting contraption – normally a less than high-tech windscreen sucker with a bracket on a stick. But some devices are designed primarily or exclusively for use in the car. Probably the best known and arguably the most attractive is the TomTom GO, a self-contained unit that can be mounted on the dashboard or windscreen and removed for safe-keeping while not in active service. It has a touch screen, a reassuringly loud voice, weighs in at 310g and runs off the car battery via the cigarette lighter. It also has an integrated Lithium-Ion battery so you could conceivably use it while on foot or bike.

Maps of the local region come on a memory card with others available on CD. In the UK, for instance, you get street-level GB (but not, apparently, Northern Ireland or Eire) coverage on a 128MB card, with major European routes on the CD. To load these, connect the TomTom to a PC via USB and transfer data from the disc. You can also download and install third-party localised 'points of interest' packages that provide details of pubs, cash points, cinemas, monuments and, er, speed cameras (see **www.pocketgps.co.uk/tomtompoi.php** and **www.poihandler.com**).

Pop it on the dashboard and away you go with a TomTom GO.

PART  # Plug-and-drive

Like the TomTom GO, a Navman iCN 650 is ready to run straight out of the box. This is another in-car device that has its own hard drive with street-level mapping detail across most of Europe. There is no integrated battery so this is strictly a model for powering through the cigarette lighter. Let's see one in situ and in action.

Most in-car GPS units come with a mounting bracket of some description. In the case of the Navman iCN 650, this attaches to the windscreen by means of a suction cup. You might choose to leave this permanently in place and simply remove the Navman when you leave the car, but it does tell potential burglars that you use a GPS unit (and it doesn't take too much savvy to guess that the unit itself has probably been stashed in the glove box or tucked under a seat). An empty bracket may still cost you a broken window.

The Navman plugs into the car's cigarette lighter. As mentioned already, this model has no internal battery. One consequence of this is that if you stall the car or stop for petrol, the Navman stops working. This is irritating but not fatal behaviour, as the internal hard disk saves information as you go along and allows you to resume from where you left off. Similarly, you can program a route in the house while the unit is connected to the mains power, whereupon it will provide driving directions when you switch it on again in the car.

3

Slotted into its bracket, you can position the unit to face towards the driver or, preferably, a front-seat passenger. At the risk of nannying, we'll stress once again that it's downright dangerous to watch a GPS screen while driving, all the more so because it's just so compelling. Like most models designed for use in the car, the Navman issues verbal directions as you go along ('In 500 metres, turn left ...') so you needn't watch the screen at all. In fact, the opening screen warns that you must not operate the unit while driving(!) and forces you to acknowledge this with a press of the OK button.

4

Tempting though it might be to tuck the unit out of sight somewhere lower down the car console, the problem is that the in-built GPS antenna needs a clear view to the sky above. The receiver is contained in a pop-out flap, seen here looking through the windscreen from the outside. This flap includes a socket for connecting an external antenna, an optional extra which you may need if your car's windscreen has a reflective UV coating.

5

The controls on the front panel let you plot routes, enter locations, search maps, switch views, tweak preferences and so forth. There's also a small remote control (again, strictly for passenger use). As soon as the receiver homes in on GPS satellites, it displays your current position on a map; and if you tell it where you want to go, it will provide turn-by-turn directions. Pick a voice – male or female – and a language and away you go.

Here's a quick look at what to expect when using this or a similar GPS unit for in-car navigation and route-planning:

Set your preferences and the software will plot the most appropriate route from A to B.

With street-level mapping detail, you can plot a route directly to the door.

An on-screen keyboard lets you enter address details for route-finding.

You may find a map distracting, in which case turn-by-turn directions are easier to follow.

Enter a destination for automatic satellite navigation with maps, instructions and verbal commands.

Variable zoom levels let you view the road ahead in close-up detail or see the bigger picture for an overview.

Step-by-step view is a useful at-a-glance model of what's coming next, complemented by verbal directions.

When you have maps that span several countries, as with the Navman iCN 650's European coverage, it's possible to include overseas travel in your routes.

A topographical map gives you a bird's eye view of the road ahead as you drive.

Most mapping software comes with points of interest (POI) pre-installed, such as the location of petrol stations and train stations. But you can also download and install your own.

PART

Mobile entertainment and content

MOBILE ENTERTAINMENT AND CONTENT

Fun and games with a PDA

PDAs began as electronic organisers and address books, and then developed in power and sophistication until they could run streamlined versions of mainstream PC software. It was then only a short step to the birth of the multimedia PDA: a handheld device that can play digital music and videos, display still photographs and slideshows, be used as an electronic book or treated as a portable games console.

All iPAQ Pocket PCs are equipped to play both sound and video, as are most Palm PCs apart from the entry-level Zire 21 (no audio or video) and the budget Zire 31 (audio only).

Pictures in your pocket

The more you pay for your PDA, the more multimedia features it is likely to have. Any machine with a colour screen can be used as a portable photo album, but serious multimedia devices such as the iPAQ 3715 and PalmOne Zire 72 have their own built-in digital cameras so they can take pictures too.

Video clips can be replayed with the same ease as still pictures. To view them on a Pocket PC you can either use Windows Media Player or a separate program such as Pocket TV, the Classic version of which plays MPEG-1 video files and can be downloaded free of charge for personal use from **www.pockettv.com**. If you want to convert your own home movies into a suitable format for Pocket PCs you can do so with Windows Movie Maker, which is available free of charge from **www.microsoft.com/windowsxp/downloads**.

It's also possible to adapt full-length feature films for playback on a Pocket or Palm PC by compressing them to a screen size of

Windows Media Player on the Pocket PC will be immediately familiar to Windows users.

Taking a picture using the built-in camera on an iPAQ rx3715.

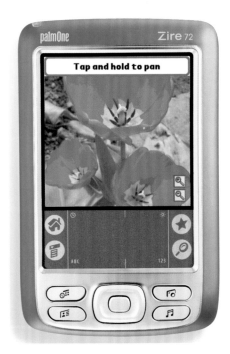
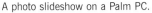

A photo slideshow on a Palm PC.

Taking a picture using the built-in camera on a PalmOne Zire 72.

Video playback on a Palm PC.

320 x 240 or smaller and saving them in an appropriate format for the player in your PDA (usually WMV, MPEG-1 or ASF). Strictly speaking this is illegal, but if you've bought the DVD version of a movie it's unlikely you'll be pursued by Interpol for making a personal copy for your PDA. There is a downside, though. Apart from the fact that many movies don't look their best on a tiny handheld screen, they require a lot of storage space, so think in terms of a 256MB of expansion card memory for every hour of high-quality video.

Palm PCs such as the Zire 72 are equipped with a media application that displays pictures and plays videos, but Palm PCs without this feature can play videos with the help of a third party program such as Kinoma Player 3 from **www.kinoma.com**. Videos are imported to a Palm PC using HotSync together with either Palm Desktop or Quick Install (depending which version of the Palm OS you're using). Regardless of their original format, videos emerge on the Palm PC as Windows ASF movies. The conversion into this format may take many minutes.

Sounding off

If you can't afford an iPod and a PDA, never mind: your multimedia PDA can function as a pretty neat MP3 player. Admittedly it can't store your entire music collection because you're limited to what will fit on a memory expansion card; but at roughly 1MB per minute for high quality MP3s, an affordable 250MB memory card will hold more than four hours of music (or double this if you don't mind lower-quality audio). With a 1GB memory card, you can store 300–500 tracks, according to the compression rate chosen.

The default Pocket PC application for MP3 playback is Windows Media Player, while on multimedia Palm PCs it's RealOne Media Player. However, there are plenty of freeware and

Like Only Lovers Can
Ed Harcourt
Here Be Monsters

MP3 playback in RealOne Player.

Snails is an original action/strategy
game for both Pocket PC and
Palm PC (seen here in its Pocket
PC version).

shareware alternatives available for both platforms. Music can be
played in the background while you get on with other tasks and
you can organise your music into playlists just as you do with a
dedicated portable player.

Almost any set of stereo earphones will work with your PDA
and you can also plug a PDA into any of the miniature speaker
sets designed for portable playback devices. Although PDAs have
their own tiny integrated speakers, these are really designed for
practical applications and you'd have to have wooden ears to
enjoy listening to music through them.

All in the Game

We'd be lying if we said that owning a PDA was the equivalent of
having a PlayStation 2 in your pocket but nevertheless there's a
diverting range of games and puzzles you can play on your PDA.
Some of them are very addictive. Solitaire is included with Palm
and Pocket PCs, and with Pocket PCs you also get the
Jawbreaker puzzle. But that's nothing: there are literally
thousands of other games available from third parties.

Most of them are derivative of the early years of PC gaming, so
you can expect to find a host of card and board games, including
poker, Monopoly and Scrabble. Another popular category is
simulations of popular pastimes such as snooker, pool and golf
and then there are the arcade rip-offs of old favourites such as
Space Invaders, Tetris and PacMan. Depending on your age, you
can relive your childhood or find out what your dad means when
he says they don't make games like that anymore!

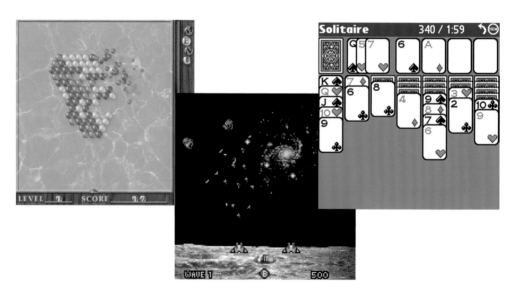

A selection of typical Palm PC
games

The written (and spoken) word

The power of language has not been diminished by digital
technology and there are now more ways than ever to enjoy your
favourite authors, books and publications. Thousands of
electronic books (ebooks) are available on the web free of charge,
while the latest best-sellers can be bought for much less than
their print equivalents. Software for reading ebooks is supplied
with both Pocket and Palm PCs, and there are commercial
offerings such as eReader (**www.ereader.com**).

Reading ebooks is easy: just tap the screen to turn the page.
You can go backwards and forwards, search for words and
phrases, and view text in a range of sizes. Just bear in mind that

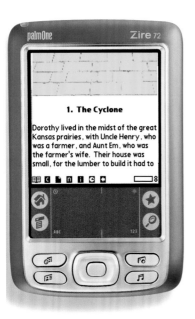

The Wizard of Oz *as it appears in Palm Reader.*

commercial books are published in different formats for specific readers, so make sure you download the correct files. Most of the free ebooks are text or HTML files you can use them on any computing device.

The primary source of free ebooks (over 13,000 of them) is Project Gutenberg at **www.gutenberg.org**. Here you'll also find a more limited range of spoken ebooks in MP3 format. For the latest bestsellers in spoken format the place to start is the subscription service at **www.audible.com**. Audible player is included with many PDAs but if you haven't got a copy, you can download it free from Audible's website.

A neat combination of the printed and digital worlds is provided by AvantGo. This is a service that enables you to carry your favourite web pages and magazines around with you on your PDA. Actually, this paints slightly too rosy a picture because what you really get is a set of channels rather than your pick of individual web pages and publications. The channels are provided by major information-gathering organisations such as CNN, the BBC and Eurosport.

You don't need a permanent, active internet connection to use AvantGo: up-to-date pages are downloaded to your mobile device whenever you synchronise with your host PC or server, and then you can read them offline wherever you are. It goes without saying that the host PC must have a live internet connection during the actual synchronisation. Up to 2MB of regularly updated content is provided free of charge, while for a modest fee you can upgrade to 8MB. Most users find 2MB is ample, provided they regularly keep their channels up to date.

To use AvantGo you need a program called AvantGo Client on your PDA. If this software is not provided with your PDA you can download it free of charge for Pocket PCs, Palm PCs and for a number of mobile phones from the AvantGo website at **www.avantgo.com**. A visit to the AvantGo website is a must anyway, because before you can choose your channels you are obliged to register at the site.

Buy bestsellers to read on your PDA at **www.ereader.com**.

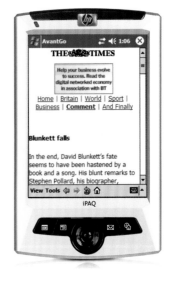

A Pocket PC-sized newspaper courtesy of AvantGo.

Audible books at **www.audible.com**.

Using AvantGo on a Pocket PC

We'll look at live internet-style content on p.145 but for now here's the best way to get reading material onto your PDA or mobile phone.

To activate AvantGo, place your Pocket PC in its cradle (or make sure that Bluetooth synchronising is active) and then start up ActiveSync on the host PC in the usual way. Click the Options button. In the Options dialog box, select the Sync Options tab. Scroll down the list of items to find AvantGo and tick its checkbox. A pop-up message will fill you in on some of the AvantGo basics. Click OK when you've read it and then click OK to start synchronising a range of pre-defined web pages from the AvantGo site. This may take several minutes, depending on the speed of your internet connection.

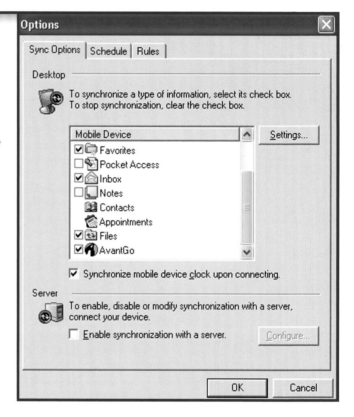

On the host PC, fire up Internet Explorer and go to **www.avantgo.com***. Click the Get it now! button to register as an AvantGo user. On the first page provide a few basic details about yourself, including an email address. On the second, choose the type of information to which you wish to subscribe to. You'll be asked for yet more personal information, which AvantGo uses for targeted advertising and to help tailor the channels it offers. On the third page, agree to the AvantGo terms and conditions and click the Accept button.*

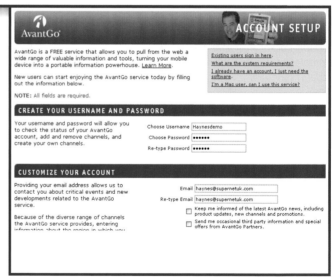

You should now have arrived at the download page, where you can specify which type of device you'll be using with the AvantGo software. Even if your PDA already has AvantGo client software installed, it's worth downloading the latest version from the site because AvantGo is subject to almost as many revisions as Windows has updates. When you have selected the appropriate software, click the Continue button.

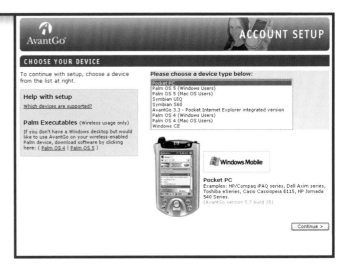

On the next screen, click the Download button and opt to save the file rather than run it. Make a note of the filename, which varies according to the version you've chosen to download. Also make a note of the folder in which it is stored. Once the download is in progress, close Internet Explorer. On completion of the download, navigate to the folder where the file is stored and double-click the file to start installation.

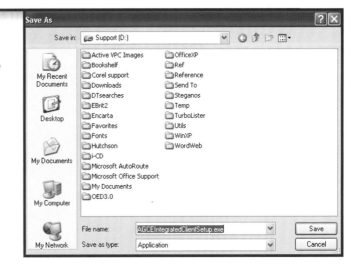

Follow the installation instructions. If permission is requested to overwrite any read-only files, click Yes. Once the program has been unpacked onto the host PC's hard disk, transfer to the Pocket PC commences. Click Yes to accept installation into the default Pocket PC folder (directory) and then click OK. On completion, remove the Pocket PC from its cradle, press the soft reset button and replace the device in its cradle. Back on the host PC, the installation software should have fired up Internet Explorer and returned you to the AvantGo website. Here you will be requested to log in again with the password you created in Step 1.

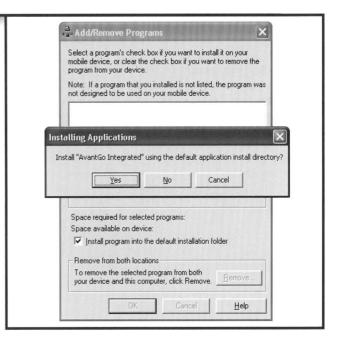

Follow the instructions to synchronise your Pocket PC. When the process has completed, click the Continue button on the web page. This takes you to a configuration screen where you must click the Configure Device button to check that your PDA's newly installed software is fully functional. There are several self-explanatory dialog boxes concerned with the configuration process. (If you see one like this, it means that other Pocket PCs are synchronised with the same host PC, so make sure you select yours and not somebody else's.) When you are warned that the current device profile already exists – this is because it has already been synchronised with AvantGo – choose the option to replace the existing profile and then click Next. On successful conclusion of the test, click Done, followed by Finish. This takes you back to the Configure Device screen where you should click the Continue button.

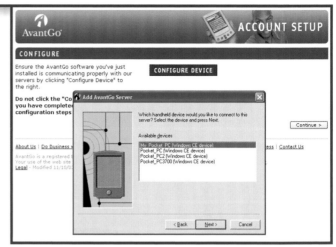

Based on the personal information and preferences you provided earlier, AvantGo now offers you a customised list of channels to choose from. Tick the channels you wish to receive and click the Continue button. This leads you to the screen shown here, which displays all the channels you have chosen together with the ones that AvantGo has selected for you. If you wish to remove any of them, click the dustbin next to its entry. All that remains now is to click the Sync button in ActiveSync for one final time. This will download your tailored channel selections.

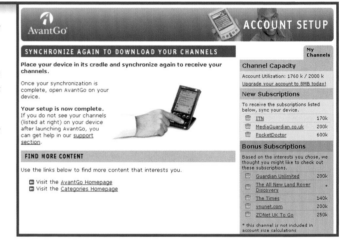

After synchronisation, you are ready to view AvantGo channels on your Pocket PC. Open the Start menu and select Programs, then tap the AvantGo icon. Enter your user name and password if it is requested. Navigating through AvantGo channels is virtually identical to navigating web pages in Internet Explorer but there are three additional tabs at the top of the AvantGo Home screen. Using these you can add or remove channels, modify your account settings and get help and support. All the changes you make on these tabs will be implemented the next time you use ActiveSync.

PART  Live content

One of the great changes heralded by third-generation telephone networks is the arrival of live content on mobile devices i.e. content that you can access across a fast wireless telephone network whenever you want.

Here we are accessing Orange UK's 3G content service on a mobile phone. From the home page, you can go straight to the portal, select your poison, check the costs and download content to your handset. If you stream a video, you see it only once; if you download it, a copy is sent to your device.

In fact, the networks have pinned everything on the assumption that you will want, nay *need* this content, and be prepared to pay through the nose for it. It's all very well being able to play MP3s on your mobile phone or even download email to a BlackBerry, but what we really want, so goes the theory, is the equivalent of the world wide web on our handheld devices.

No, really ...

OK, we can tell you're not convinced, but consider this: when you've used a BlackBerry for a few days, the thought of *not* having continual, easy, instant, global access to email becomes suddenly unthinkable, or close to it. Similarly, when you make the change from dial-up internet access to broadband, the real revelation is not so much the increase in speed but rather the fact that the internet is suddenly just there, on tap, around the clock. As wireless networks expand, it's entirely possible that we'll simply come to expect ubiquitous internet access. We might get online through 3G or Wi-Fi or Bluetooth, or with some other technology entirely, but we probably won't give a second thought to the mechanics (and quite right too). Most likely in the short term is a scenario in which networks and technologies overlap and our mobile devices switch seamlessly among them as required. The shape of these devices will doubtless change completely, with smartphones, PDAs, BlackBerrys, Tablet PCs and all the rest evolving, mutating and occasionally improving. But it's a sure thing that most of us will have *some* kind of multifunctional mobile gadget and safe to assume that its primary function will be to keep us permanently connected not just to a mobile phone network but also to the internet.

Right now, a fantastic amount of effort and money is being expended on wireless networks. But for this to continue, the network providers have to start making some money out of us consumers. This brings us back to content. If all you do with your mobile device is make phone calls, access email and Google the odd web search, you aren't going to download much data – and that, in the world of GPRS and 3G, means you aren't going to generate big bills. That's no good at all.

So the networks must persuade us to do more. Now, you may be sitting out there with a sceptical head on thinking, 'Hmm, it's all very well, this mobile technology, but I can't even get my head around text messaging and I really don't need anything fancier.' We tend to agree, but rest assured that the networks and content providers are gunning hard for our custom. Sooner or later, they'll ensnare us all with a cunningly crafted mobile killer application that we discover we just can't live without.

Perhaps. In fact, it's just as likely that a must-have mobile application will explode out of nowhere, taking everybody by surprise. After all, nobody, but nobody, predicted the phenomenal success of text messaging and who would have guessed the unfathomable craze for mobile phone ring tones?

Targeted content like the
Premiership-action 'Match Centre'
service from BlueStar Mobile
(**www.bluestarmobile.com**) is
designed to draw in the punters.

Building bridges

One important issue or dilemma that's going to play out over the
coming months and years is the difference between network-
specific content and cross-network content. For instance, let's say
that if you subscribe to the T-Mobile network, you get to watch
exclusive clips of premiership football action. This is possible
because T-Mobile sponsors a few Premier League clubs and, in
return, has exclusive access to footage, player and manager
interviews, analyses and stats and more.

Now, for the football fan who needs a mobile phone in any
case, this is a clear incentive to sign up with T-Mobile rather than
with, say, Vodafone or Orange (at least if he supports one of the
sponsored clubs). T-Mobile's sponsorship thus pays off at least in
part in terms of new business. On the other hands, though,
T-Mobile knows that it can market (i.e. sell) this content to non-
subscribers too. Plenty of Vodafone customers will want to see
the clips of their favourite teams but not all will switch networks.
Particularly if they're currently tied to a 12-month contract.

So what T-Mobile can do is actually threefold:
- Offer exclusive football content to lure new subscribers.
- Build access to this content into flexible payment plans.
  Weekly clips and interviews may be completely free to
  subscribers but the network can also offer specific events on a
  pay-per-view basis. A subscriber might, for instance, be offered
  blow-by-blow text messaging commentary of an important

match for free but also have the opportunity to watch the
match live on his phone or mobile device for a fee.
- Offer the same or a limited version of this content to non-
  subscribers, but for a higher fee.

A mobile network operator's natural tendency is to develop its
own supposedly indispensable content and to enter into exclusive
deals with content providers and partners. But the reality is that
Joe Public hates artificial barriers. Imagine if you could only
access BBC websites if AOL was your ISP. Imagine if you could
only email people in the same city as you. It would be a
nonsense. In the mobile sphere, it looks like we'll see a great
deal of network-specific content at the outset but the balance will
almost certainly shift towards similar content for all. The
difference will be how, and how much, we pay for it all.

If there's any sanity in the world, we will also see an end to
network incompatibilities where phone X only works on network
Y. Come to think of it, we'd also like to see an end to the absurd
and outmoded practice of 'locking' phones so that they work only
on the network that sells them. Pricing needs to be harmonised
so that it's transparent, it's affordable and you only get one
monthly bill that covers everything, even when you access
content provided by a rival network. Flat-fee pricing (all the
content you want for a fixed monthly cost) is also going to prove
much more appealing than the current pay-per-megabyte policies
on GPRS and 3G.

What's in the pipeline?

We're quite some way off these goals but meanwhile here are some pointers about what to expect on the content front. Chances are you'll find this most appealing if you're aged between 18 and 24, because that puts you firmly at the heart of the ensuing content charm offensive.

Streaming video

You can already watch video clips and even full-length movies on a mobile device, subject to memory capacity, but how about catching the 6 o'clock news live at 6 o'clock on your phone or PDA? Or receiving breaking news video clips throughout the day? Or watching a sell-out concert live? Or tuning in to a unique sporting event?

Video conferencing

Face-to-face chat with video. No more pretending to be working late in the office when you're really calling home from the pub.

Music downloads

When you can't get a song out of your head, download it from an online music retailer and get it onto your mobile device instead.

Radio

Virgin Radio was the first to broadcast over 3G. It works in stereo over all networks anywhere in the world and is entirely free.

Instant messaging

When the connection is always-on, it's easy to conduct real-time two-way text chat. More flexible than text messaging; less intrusive than a phone call.

Games

You can already download and play quite outstanding games on mobile devices, but high-speed networks make live multi-player gaming a real possibility. Boost your superstar status in the global gaming leagues while waiting for the bus.

Blogging

A blog is a personal website that you update every day or even every hour of every day. The phenomenon attracts niche commentators who compete with one another to be first to publish the news in their specialist field. Blogging from a mobile device holds obvious appeal.

Adult content

Yes, somewhat inevitably, mobile porn is going to be huge and probably very, very profitable.

Capture the action as it happens on a handheld.

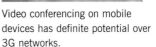

Video conferencing on mobile devices has definite potential over 3G networks.

Free high-quality music, anywhere, with Virgin.

MOBILE ENTERTAINMENT AND CONTENT

Portable Media Centres

Did somebody whisper 'first generation'? That's perhaps the best way to sum up the current crop of PMC devices, or Portable Media Centres.

What we're talking about are gadgets that do for movies what MP3 players did for music i.e. make it truly portable. The idea is that you can either record programs or films directly from a TV or transfer them onto the device from a computer and thereafter watch them on an integrated colour screen. For keeping kids happy during a long journey, they're fantastic; but are they anything more than toys?

Movies and more on the move

It's perfectly possible to watch video on most PDAs or smartphones but the real problem is storage space. Even in a highly compressed format like DivX (**www.divx.com**), full-length feature films are just too big for all but the highest-capacity memory cards. Besides, do you really want to watch a movie on a phone-sized screen?

The PMC premise is that you're better off with a dedicated device that has:
● An internal hard disk, so storage space is no longer an issue.
● A large, bright screen.
● Sufficient battery life to get you through a film or a flight.

A PMC worth its salt will also play MP3 music files and showcase digital images. But beyond such shared ground, there are significant differences. Here we glance at two current models, both of which we expect to be rapidly replaced with superior versions.

Larger than a PDA but smaller than a portable DVD player – that's the appeal of a PMC.

Menus, movies, pictures, games and more on a Mustek.

Creative Zen PMC

This device is designed primarily for watching recordings of TV programmes made on a home entertainment PC running Microsoft Windows Media Center. If you're unfamiliar with the Media Center concept (in which case you should buy the *Haynes Home Entertainment Manual*), it's basically a computer designed to sit under the telly and function as a digital video recorder (and music player and much, much more). The Creative PMC lets you take recorded shows with you on the road.

The Creative Zen PMC: portable, yes; pocketable, not really.

The Zen approach has a decidedly Windows feel about it, which is natural when you consider that it's designed to be a mobile partner for the Media Center software for desktops.

Mustek PVR-H140

In contrast, the Mustek model can connect directly to a TV, VCR or DVD player and make its own recordings. It's a portable video recorder, in other words, ideal for copying movies or grabbing an episode of your favourite TV series. It is also possible to transfer video files directly from a computer but only if they are first converted to an acceptable file format (of which there is only one: ASF). Supplied software takes care of the conversion but it's a slow process.

The Mustek PVR-H140 lacks finesse, particularly in the finishing, but it's good for a first-generation device.

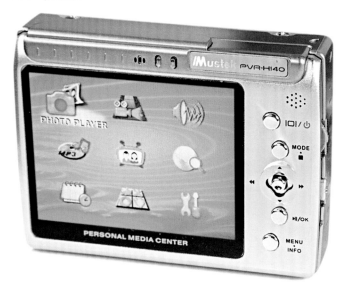

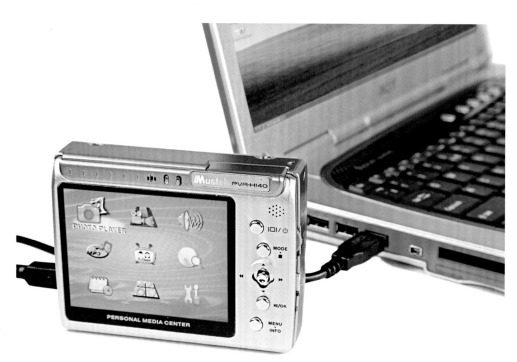

Hook up your PMC to a PC and transfer movies, music and pictures for enjoyment on the road. It just might keep you sane in a strange hotel in a strange land.

The future?

We reckon that portable media centres are here to stay. In fact, they're actually pretty desirable companions for a mobile worker. For instance, these two models and others like them can play music and showcase digital photographs as well as play (and, in the Mustek's case, record) video. But the current problem is one of bulk. The Zen is the bigger, heavier device despite having only half the storage space – 20GB compared to the H140's 40GB – but neither could seriously be described as pocket-sized.

The idea is a good one but we suspect that PMCs will really take off when they are designed with the flair of an iPod and are light enough to carry in a trouser pocket. But you can see the complications coming, can't you? Just like smartphones and PDAs, there's a tricky balance between screen size, which must be large enough to make video playback pleasurable, and weight. There's also the choice between the limited capacity of memory card storage and huge but heavy internal hard disks. And then, of course, manufacturers are sure to build in home networking capability (with and without cables), USB and/or FireWire for PC connections, Bluetooth, office applications, games and – inevitably – mobile phone functionality. In fact, hang on for a couple of months and you'll be able to download fresh video content straight onto your PMC's hard disk across a wireless 3G network while simultaneously watching last night's sitcom, chatting to one colleague, instant messaging another and plotting your route with the integrated GPS receiver ...

Ah, sometimes you just yearn for the simple life ...

Anyone for an iPod? It may only do one thing but it does it rather well.

8

PART 8

MOBILE TECHNOLOGY MANUAL

Appendices

Appendix 1 – Mobile accessories

It's amazing how many add-ons, upgrades and extras are available for PDAs. Even though a PDA is meant to fit in your pocket, if you bought all the available accessories you'd need a suitcase to carry them around – and another full of cash to buy them!

One way of categorising expansion devices is by how they attach to the PDA. Typically this is via a Secure Digital (SD) or a CompactFlash (CF) expansion slot. However, there are some devices which plug into the USB connector or audio output jack and there are others that need no physical connection at all because they communicate wirelessly via Bluetooth or Wi-Fi.

In the following overview of the gadgets and gizmos that can help you get more out of your PDA, we've grouped them according to what they do rather than how they're connected.

Memory upgrades

Having more memory enables you to install more programs and store more data on your Pocket PC or Palm PC. PDAs don't need the vast amounts of memory you find in the average desktop PC, so the addition of even an extra 64MB can make a significant difference. You really can't have too much memory if you intend to use your PDA as a mobile media player for music, video or still images.

There are two main types of memory for PDAs: CompactFlash (CF) and Secure Digital (SD). CF cards come in capacities of up to 4GB and are generally cheaper than SD cards but are also more bulky. The larger capacities are supplied on a type II card, which is thicker than a type I card, so it's important to check that your PDA has a type II slot if you're thinking of buying anything over 1GB. Fortunately the larger type II slot can also accept type I cards.

SD cards are not much bigger than postage stamps, though considerably thicker. They have a slider control on the side that protects their contents from being overwritten and they include copy protection mechanisms so that software and music can be supplied on them without danger of it being pirated.

CompactFlash memory modules of up to 1GB are readily available and reasonably priced, but more expensive modules up to 4GB can also be purchased.

SD memory modules are small, light and reliable. Their only shortcoming is that it's possible to accidentally move the data protection lock when inserting them.

Buying memory from the supplier of your PDA is not the cheapest way of obtaining it.

There's an older, slower and generally inferior type of memory called Multimedia Card (MMC). It uses the same physical format as SD memory, but is best avoided. MMC cards are virtually unavailable in sizes over 64MB.

Another unusual memory format is the Sony Memory Stick family, comprising the original Memory Stick and two sophisticated newcomers called Memory Stick Pro and Memory Stick Select. These are developed jointly by Sony and SanDisk. This type of memory is used in many Sony entertainment devices, including the Sony CLIÉ multimedia PDAs (now discontinued in many parts of the world).

When buying CD or SD cards, you are not restricted to those sold by the maker of your PDA. In fact, the cards from HP and PalmOne are among the most expensive on the market. Feel free to shop around for bargains, but avoid ultra-cheap unbranded memory cards if you can. Not all cards are created equal: some work faster than others and the branded cards tend to be more rigorously checked to ensure they're not dead on arrival.

Wireless cards

More and more PDAs are being sold with either Bluetooth or Wi-Fi built into them. However, both forms of communication can be added to any PDA with SD or CF slots, so you don't have to trade in your old PDA just because you want wireless connectivity.

Wi-Fi is the obvious choice if your main aim is to connect to a private or public network, but with the more versatile Bluetooth you can:

● Use wireless Bluetooth headsets to make phone calls or listen to music.
● Print using Bluetooth-enabled printers.

● Surf the web and send and receive emails using your Bluetooth-enabled phone as a wireless modem.
● Surf, email and synchronise files by connecting to your modem-equipped PC. Your PC will need a Bluetooth USB card to enable it to talk to the PDA.
● Connect to the internet via a Bluetooth access point. This is a box of tricks that broadcasts a wireless internet signal to PCs and PDAs within a limited range.
● Connect via Bluetooth to a modem plugged into an ordinary phone socket somewhere else in the same room or building.

A minor snag with both Bluetooth and Wi-Fi expansion cards is that they protrude slightly from the PDA, making it a little less portable. Another is that if you only have one expansion slot, you can't plug in a wireless card and a memory upgrade card at the same time. Of course, there's nothing to stop you changing cards according to the task in hand, but an even better solution is to buy one of the new breed of expansion cards which incorporate both wireless communication facilities and extra memory on the same plug-in CF or SD card.

A Bluetooth Compact Flash adapter from Belkin (**www.belkin.com**).

A Wi-Fi (802.11b) wireless networking SD card from Pretec (**www.pretec.com**)

Combining a Wi-Fi card with 128MB of memory sidesteps the limitation of a single CompactFlash expansion slot (**www.sandisk.com**).

For PDAs with just a single SD expansion slot, a combined Wi-Fi and 256MB memory card from SanDisk is a smart solution (**www.sandisk.com**).

The Veo Photo Traveler for Palm PCs is supplied with a rugged travel case to keep it safe when not in use.

The Veo Photo Traveler 130S is designed for Pocket PCs. It can film video clips as well as take still pictures.

The Pretec SmartCam (**www.pretec.com**) is a 1.3 megapixel camera that can also take movies. Its main claim to fame is that it works with both Pocket PCs and Palm PCs using Palm OS version 5 or later.

Cameras

Pocket PCs and Palm PCs with built-in cameras are readily available, but add-on cameras can be used with any device that has an SD or CF expansion slot.

For instance, the Veo Photo Traveler for Palm PCs (full details from **www.veo.com**) fits into the SDIO expansion slot. It has a swivel lens with manually adjustable focus. The resolution is 640 x 480 pixels, which, while no great shakes compared to a dedicated digital camera, produces very crisp pictures when viewed on a Palm PC.

For the Pocket PC with an SDIO expansion slot, the Veo Photo Traveler 130S offers an optical resolution of 1.3 megapixels. This is equivalent to the 1280 x 1024 resolution most of us are used to seeing on a 17-inch monitor. Fitted with a swivel lens, self-timer and 4x digital zoom, the camera comes with its own protective travel bag.

Keyboards

The best way of getting significant amounts of text into a PDA is to pipe it over from your PC during the synchronising process but if you're the sort of person who also needs to do a fair amount of data entry while out on the road with your PDA, the solution could be a portable keyboard.

Most PDA keyboards can be folded, some of them several times to a size no bigger than the PDA itself, but when opened

The PDA support unit of the Stowaway Universal Bluetooth keyboard (**www.thinkoutside.com**) can be detached and positioned for maximum viewing comfort. When folded, the entire keyboard can be slipped in a bag or pocket.

Both Palm and HP sell their own keyboards if you want to buy from the manufacturer of your PDA.

out they're about the size of the average laptop keyboard. Very early models were designed to fit into the serial synchronisation port of the PDA itself, which meant buying the right keyboard for your particular model. There are also universal keyboards that use infrared rather than a physical connection. The PDA is located on a stand combined with the keyboard and its infrared beam is aligned with a sensor built into the keyboard stand. The most recent innovation in keyboards is the use of Bluetooth which, because it does not rely on a line-of-sight infrared connection, permits the design of keyboards that give the user total flexibility to arrange the keyboard and PDA into the most comfortable and practical positions.

Keyboards are available from a number of specialist companies and from HP and PalmOne to match specific models of their machines. PalmOne even does a thumb-operated keyboard for its i705 PDA. This slides over the bottom of the PDA and connects to the serial synchronisation port. HP has a similar keyboard suitable for use with its rz1700, hx2000 and hx4700 ranges.

One of the most popular keyboards is the Think Outside Stowaway Universal Bluetooth keyboard (**www.thinkoutside.com**). It can be used with Pocket PCs and many Symbian mobile phones, but not with Palm PCs.

The Logitech KeyCase is a smart and stylish all-in-one keyboard and protective case for M-series Palm PCs. Unroll the keyboard, slide the SmartMotion cradle upright and you're ready to type. It's no bigger than a wallet when it's rolled up (**www.logitech.com**).

Printing and networking

One of the best things the right accessories will help you do with a Pocket PC or Palm PC is print directly to a desktop printer. Oddly enough, neither type of PDA was designed for printing, so none of the built-in Palm or Windows programs sports a Print command. The reason for this apparent omission is that printing was seen as an unnecessary function for the simpler types of PDA, which were mainly used as address books. But now that PDAs are used to edit Word, Excel and other business documents, it is no longer convenient to wait until documents have been piped over to a desktop PC before printing them.

There's more than one approach to direct printing, but the key to all of them is Bluetooth, which means you need a Bluetooth-enabled PDA and a Bluetooth-enabled printer. However, before worrying about making a printer connection, there's the tiny problem of adding a Print command to your PDA's software. For Pocket PCs this is easy and free: just visit the HP Mobile Printing web pages at **www.hp.com/go/pocketpcprint_software** and download the correct version of the print utility for your PDA. Palm PC users will need to buy a third-party print utility, such as PrintBoy from **www.bachmannsoftware.com**.

With a print utility installed, you can print directly to any printer equipped with a Bluetooth adapter. Pentax sell a neat range of portable printing and scanning devices aimed at laptop and PDA users. The PocketJet II and PocketJet 200 printers are powered by rechargeable batteries, print on special paper at up to three pages per minute and are compatible with most PDAs, PCs and BlackBerry devices. Although they are not themselves Bluetooth equipped, they are supplied with a cable which allows them to be connected to a third-party Bluetooth printer adapter.

If you don't need a portable printer, you can add a Bluetooth printer adapter to your existing desktop printer. Belkin sells a

The Pentax PocketJet II prints at 300 dots per inch and the PocketJet 200 at 200dpi. Both are completely portable (**www.pentax.com**).

Wireless USB Printer Adapter that converts any USB printer, inkjet or laser, into a Bluetooth device. You can then print directly from your PDA.

If you want to go one step further, you can link your PDA to the internet and add up to two Bluetooth-enabled printers to a home network with the Belkin Bluetooth Access Point. This gadget connects to your wired home network via a standard Ethernet cable. It has two USB ports into which you can plug standard inkjet or laser printers and it acts as a Bluetooth access point for any Bluetooth device within range. When you link a Bluetooth PDA, the access point assigns the PDA the necessary IP address and DNS information so that it can connect directly to the internet without further ado. This is very much easier than using the Internet Connection Sharing (ICS) feature of Windows, plus you get direct access to two printers from your PDA when required.

The Belkin Wireless Printer Adapter converts any USB printer to Bluetooth operation (**www.belkin.com**).

The Belkin Bluetooth Access Point links your PDA to your wired home network, providing internet connectivity and the services of two printers at the same time (**www.belkin.com**).

This stylish red leather case from Hewlett Packard allows you to use your Pocket PC without removing it from the case (**www.hp.com**).

Something for everyone

However careful you are when using your PDA, one day it is going to mysteriously leap from your hand and plummet to the floor. Nine times out of ten it will miraculously survive with a couple of scratches, but a protective case is a sensible precaution nevertheless. These are available in universal formats or tailored for specific machines and you can buy them from any computer store or direct from the manufacturer of your PDA.

If you take your PDA with you everywhere and use it outside, a tailored case that allows you to use the device without first removing it is a good idea. Otherwise, go for a well-padded basic case or an 'executive' style folder with space and pockets for other accessories.

Although there's little likelihood of a PDA stylus ever wearing out, they're ridiculously easy to lose. Fortunately you can buy replacements cheaply from the manufacturer, usually in packs of three. Quite a few vendors have come up with special pens aimed at PDA users, often with two or three selectable ink

This executive case for a Palm Tungsten T3 includes two pockets for SD memory or SDIO expansion cards (**www.palmone.com**).

The Quadra pen incorporates three ink colours and a stylus tip (**www.belkin.com**).

The LaserWright combines a pen, stylus and laser pointer. It requires three button batteries (**www.belkin.com**).

The Stowaway mouse is designed especially for Pocket PC users (**www.thinkoutside.com**).

colours plus a stylus tip. While these are interesting gadgets, it's easy to forget which tip is in use and mistakenly try to write on your PDA's screen with a ballpoint pen or sign a letter with a blunt stylus. Fortunately, neither will do any permanent harm.

Another input device not normally associated with PDAs is the mouse. Strange as it may seem, Bluetooth mice for PDAs are available, and some die-hard Windows users seem to prefer them as a way of using their Pocket PCs. Logitech even sells a Bluetooth mouse together with a stand that doubles as both charger for the mouse and as a Bluetooth hub for the host PC. With this connected to your desktop, you have a Bluetooth mouse that can be used with your PC plus instant Bluetooth connectivity between your desktop and your PDA.

Linking your PDA to a desktop PC or network and sharing its internet connection in order to surf the web and send or receive email is cheap and easy – but what if you need to get online and there's no private or public network available? Or what if your PDA is not equipped with Bluetooth? One simple solution is a standard dial-up modem on an SD card. Plug this into your PDA's SDIO expansion socket, then attach a cable from the modem to any convenient phone socket and away you go. This is a low-tech approach but might be just what you need if you use your PDA in several interior locations but don't actually need an internet connection while you're on the move.

Not forgetting laptops ...

As we have seen, some laptops are more fully equipped than others. But virtually any portable computer can benefit from the seemingly infinite range of bolt-on, plug-in accessories. With USB and FireWire interfaces usually available, lack of choice is not an issue. And if you have an older machine that lacks both, a PC Card adapter can bring it up to speed.

But perhaps the most important factor to consider when working away from home with a portable computer is the importance of backing up important files. It's all too easy to have a laptop stolen or to leave it on a train and easier still to knock it to the ground and render it unusable. You can get industrial-strength droppable laptops ... but we'll warrant that yours isn't one of them.

Here are three suggestions. First, whenever you are connected to the internet, email copies of critical files to yourself. A Gmail account is perfect because it accepts large attachments (up to 10MB at a time) and you can later download these files onto any other computer in the world with a minimum of fuss.

Secondly, back up files to recordable CD or DVD as you go along. If your laptop doesn't have a recordable drive, use a pocket-sized external hard drive. This means that you should always have a second, safe copy of your work.

Rechargeable

Bluetooth® wireless hub

The MX900 rechargeable mouse comes on a hub that adds Bluetooth connectivity to your PC (**www.logitech.com**).

The Pretec SD modem is compatible with the latest Pocket PCs and offers fax facilities as well as a 56K connection (**www.pretec.com**).

No USB or FireWire? No problem: plug in a PC Card adapter.

Backup as you go along with a
plug-in external hard drive.

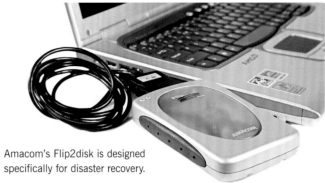

Amacom's Flip2disk is designed
specifically for disaster recovery.

Finally, for a rock-solid backup routine, consider something like
the Flip2Disk from Amacom (**www.amacom-tech.com**). This is
essentially a 100GB external hard drive that can hook up to a
laptop via USB, FireWire or the PC Card interface. Because it
draws power through the connection, its doesn't need its own
power supply. But what makes it different is the supplied
FlipBack software. When you first plug it in, it makes an initial
image (exact copy) of the laptop's hard disk. This effectively
preserves every file, folder, setting and preference. The device
then updates the image every time you connect it afresh. Should
your laptop go missing, you can connect the Flip2disk to any
other computer and access your files and folders from there; or
should your laptop's hard drive fail, perhaps following a fall, you
can replace it with the Flip2disk's own hard drive and continue
with minimal disruption.

If your laptop's built-in speakers
are too tinny and weak for decent
music or movie playback, pack a
pair of portables in your travel
bag.

Who can resist the Notebook
Accessory Value Pack from Trust
(**www.trust.com**). You get a
miniature optical mouse, a USB
hub (which turns one socket into
two), retractable telephone and
network cables, and, best of all, a
bendy light powered by USB.

PART 8

Appendix 2 – Hints and tips for PDAs

If you're the sort of individual who is understandably worried about having your life's secrets made public should you lose your PDA, relax: there is adequate password protection built into every PDA to ensure that if you lose it or have it stolen, nobody else will be able to read your personal data. Of course, you have to choose a password and set your personal preferences first ...

Read on for details of this and other tips.

Password protection

On a Pocket PC, you can set up a password that will be required every time you switch on the device. The password can be a simple 4-digit pin or a longer alphanumeric password. Obviously a long password is the only sensible option because anybody with sufficient determination can crack a 4-digit pin by sheer persistence. Entering a long password is a pain if you're using power-saving options, though, because your Pocket PC will turn itself off frequently. In this case, there's an option to nominate how long the device has to be suspended before the password kicks in. If you set this to one hour, then no password will be required until the device has been suspended for this period of time.

You can set a hint that will be used if you ever forget your password, but if you can't remember the password even with a hint your only option is to do a hard reset. This unlocks your Pocket PC but also clears all the data stored on it. This isn't something you'd want to do without a recent backup.

Password protection on a Palm PC works in much the same way and there's the same hard reset option if you forget your password. Palm PCs also offer the facility to protect individual contacts, addresses and appointments with a password by marking them as private. Records marked as private will be invisible (or masked by a grey bar) unless you know the password. The method of concealment depends on the security options chosen.

Stages in setting a password for the first time on a Palm PC.

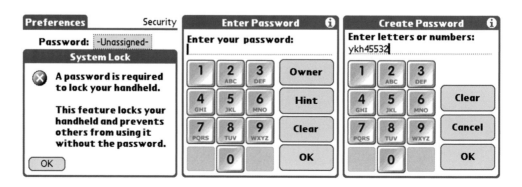

Some PDAs, such as the iPAQ 4700 and the PalmOne Zire 72, offer additional security in the form of data encryption. This kicks in automatically whenever the device is turned off and scrambles all the data. It can only be unscrambled by entering the password. Third-party encryption software with similar capabilities can be purchased for PDAs that don't come with their own encryption facility.

Devices with wireless connectivity are at risk from hackers even when they haven't been lost or stolen, so it's a good idea to always turn off Bluetooth or Wi-Fi when not in use. This also extends battery life. If you use your PDA to join a Wi-Fi network, it makes sense to ensure the network is properly set-up and firewalled using either WEP or WPA security.

Backing up

Having a complete backup of all the data and programs on your PDA is essential, as it saves you having to re-enter everything onto a new PDA if yours is lost or stolen. It also enables you to recover from a hard reset. A hard reset destroys all the data and third-party programs on a PDA, returning it to the same condition as when it left the factory. You should never have to perform a hard reset unless you forget your password ... but there is always the possibility things can go wrong.

Pocket PC users are better served than Palm owners in terms of built-in backup software. To make a complete backup of everything on your Pocket PC, all you need do is start ActiveSync, open the Tools menu and select Backup/Restore. Then you can choose whether you want to make a full or an incremental backup. Some Pocket PCs have a secondary backup facility which allows a backup to be made either to the File Store memory of the iPAQ itself, or to a memory expansion card, thus enabling you to restore from a backup without needing to use the host PC.

Palm users are not provided with a backup program. Instead, an automatic backup copy is kept on the host PC and this is updated during every use of Palm HotSync. While this is adequate to cover minor glitches, it is not a lot of help if you are replacing a lost or broken PDA. The key data may be still be there but do you really want to reinstate all your preferences, reconfigure your email and reinstall any third-party programs? The best plan is to install a program such as BackupBuddyVFS Personal (**http://bluenomad.com**). With this, a single command backs up everything on your Palm PDA to a memory expansion card. You can restore backups to the same PDA or to a new device with equal ease.

Power-saving techniques

Assuming you've managed not to lose your PDA or leave it in the pocket of your jeans on wash day or had it stolen, there is yet another factor that might prevent you from using it – lack of power.

Rechargeable slimline lithium batteries have replaced the standard alkaline batteries once used in PDAs and they're great. They're light, compact, fast-charging and long-lasting. But unlike AA batteries, you can't buy replacements at any time of the day

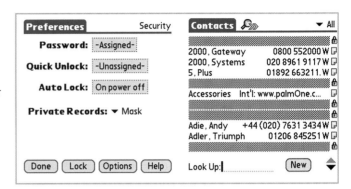

Choosing to mask private records on a Palm PC (left) results in the Contacts display on the right, where private records are concealed.

Using iPAQ Backup to store an image of a Pocket PC's memory on its expansion card.

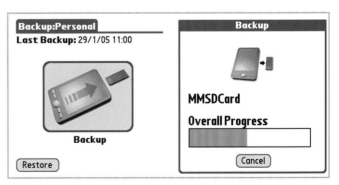

Using a commercially available program called BackupBuddyVFS to back up a Palm PC to its expansion card.

or night wherever you happen to be in the world. Good power management techniques are therefore essential, especially if you don't have a spare battery or if your PDA lacks an externally accessible battery slot. Here are some general tips:

● Turn off Bluetooth and Wi-fi when you are not using them.
● Turn down the brightness setting of the screen.
● Use the automatic brightness control if your PDA has one.
● Turn off the screen when listening to music.
● Lock your PDA's keys so it can't be turned on accidentally in your pocket.
● Turn off the beam receive feature unless you anticipate exchanging data with another device.
● Set as short a period for automatic switch-off as you can live with.
● When not in use, leave your PDA on charge so it is always fully charged when you need it.
● Keep the device switched off during charging for a faster charge.

If you think you might need to recharge your PDA while away from base, take its charger with you or buy a portable charger that you can plug into a car's cigarette lighter. USB charging cables are available that allow you to draw power from any available computer, including a laptop. Some iPAQ Pocket PCs come with this facility as standard, though to make it work you must first enable USB Charging as a system setting.

Memory management for Pocket PCs

On a desktop PC you explicitly open programs when you need them and close them when you don't. A PDA is different because even though you can only see one program at a time, there are many others ticking over in the background waiting for you to return to them. There's another difference too, which is that because a PDA has no hard disk it must permanently store in memory not only all the additional programs you've installed but also all the data you've generated.

By moving data and programs to memory expansion cards, you can ease the burden on your PDA. However, a Pocket PC still has the overhead of running Windows and Windows programs, which is much more demanding than running Palm software. Pocket PC users should therefore be more aware of how memory is being used and, occasionally, take a hand in tweaking the settings.

To make changes to the way memory is allocated, open the Start menu and tap Settings, System and Memory. The Memory screen has three tabs. Tap the Memory tab to determine how the built-in memory should be divided between storing data and running programs; tap the storage tab to see how much space remains in the iPAQ file store and on any memory expansion cards; and tap the Running Programs tab to close down any single program or all of them. Killing programs in this way can speed up a Pocket PC that seems to be gradually slowing down. Another way of releasing memory is to remove any programs you no longer use, as described on p.90–92.

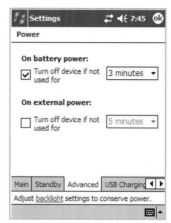

Setting power-saving options on Pocket PC.

Enabling USB charging on a Pocket PC

A Pocket PC in the process of shutting down all running programs. Sometimes stopping just one program is enough to give a boost when performance seems to be flagging.

Using a Bluetooth adapter with Windows XP and SP2

Until the introduction of the Service Pack 2 (SP2) upgrade to Windows XP late in 2004, Windows had no built-in tools for managing Bluetooth connections. Instead, third-party vendors of Bluetooth hardware supplied their own software. Unfortunately, the Bluetooth drivers in SP2 are more basic than established third-party drivers and they don't support the full range of Bluetooth activities. In particular, you can't use the SP2 drivers to synchronise a PDA with a desktop PC.

If you're thinking 'Fine, I'll stick with the third-party drivers', you'll be disappointed. The technical gurus at Microsoft are so keen on everybody using drivers that have been digitally signed by them that when you try to install a Bluetooth transceiver with third party drivers, SP2 takes over and installs its own instead. This is bad news for anybody wanting to use Bluetooth for synchronising a PDA.

But, as always, there is a workaround. This is will suffice until Microsoft gets its act together and improves its own Bluetooth drivers. Start by installing the third-party drivers and software supplied with the Bluetooth adapter. When these are overridden by the SP2 drivers, choose to update the driver but don't let Windows decide which driver to use. Instead, you must specify the older, overwritten driver, which should still be on the system. If it isn't, you can specify its location on the installation CD-ROM.

Once you've reset the driver, you'll have the full range of Bluetooth connections to choose from and you won't have to go through this rather fiddly procedure again (unless for some reason you remove and replace the Bluetooth adapter).

So much for the virtues of plug-and-play for USB adapters. In this situation it's more a case of plug-and-leave-alone-if-you-know-what's good-for-you.

The following short guide illustrates the steps required to reclaim the use of third-party Bluetooth drivers, using the example of a Belkin USB adapter. The Belkin adapter uses the same WIDCOMM profiles as most other third-party drivers, all of which are overwritten by SP2. You can use the same workaround with any of them.

Having installed Bluetooth drivers and inserted the USB adapter, there are two Bluetooth icons in the Windows Control Panel. The one named Bluetooth Configuration is a dialogue box for third party utilities and the one named Bluetooth Devices is the standard Windows SP2 dialogue box. Attempting to use the third-party utilities by double-clicking the Bluetooth Configuration icon leads to this error message, caused by Windows having overridden the third-party driver.

②

Open Device Manager (or click Start, Run, type devmgmt.msc, and click OK). Double-click the entry for Bluetooth Radios to view its contents. One entry describes the adapter and the other refers to Microsoft's Bluetooth Enumerator. Right-click on the adapter and select Update Driver.

③

In the Hardware Update Wizard, click 'No, not this time' to prevent the Wizard searching the internet for a driver. Click Next. Select 'Install from a list or specific location'. Click Next. Select 'Don't search. I will choose the driver to install'. Click Next.

④

At least two entries will be shown. The current driver is the certified Microsoft SP2 driver, which bears a green tick to show that it is has been digitally signed. Any alternative driver, when selected, will display a warning message about not being digitally signed. Click to select the appropriate third-party driver, then click Next. With any luck, because the driver has already been installed, the wizard will quickly locate and activate it. If the third-party driver cannot be found or if no alternative entry is listed, click the Have Disk button and browse to the third-party drivers on CD-ROM. On the last page of the wizard, click Finish.

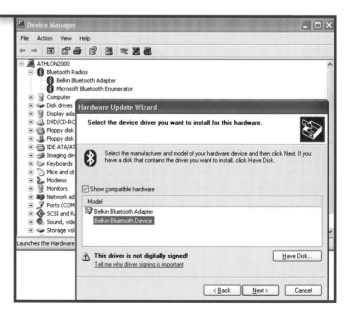

Appendix 3 – Drive-less computing

As we have seen, many lightweight notebooks treat CD/DVD drives as optional extras, the idea being that you can keep the weight down by detaching the drive when it's not required.

Sometimes you just need a CD ... but that doesn't mean that you necessarily need a CD drive.

Unfortunately, if you need to access CDs or DVD discs when on the move, even infrequently, you may find yourself lugging along the drive while you travel. Of course, if it's simply data that you need, you can easily copy files from disc to the notebook's hard drive. However, this approach doesn't work for programs that require a CD or DVD to run, such as route-planning software or CD-ROM-based encyclopaedias or, perhaps more importantly, computer games. In other words, any program that requires you to keep a disc in the drive while it's running is a potential problem.

The ideal solution would be to have a drive-less notebook that can nevertheless play CDs and DVDs as if it had the requisite hardware. What you need, it seems, is a 'virtual' CD or DVD drive. What you need is Alcohol 52%. Here's why.

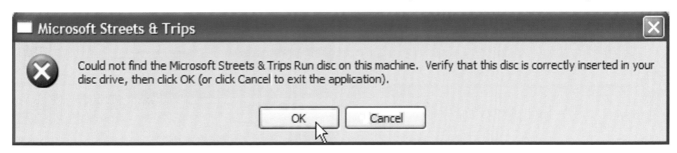

Working with a virtual drive
In this step-by-step, we'll create a virtual CD drive and then copy a CD to the laptop's hard drive in the form of a disc image. This lets you do two things: access whatever data is on the CD without recourse to the physical media and, in the case of programs and games, run them very much more quickly. The latter is possible because the computer can read data from the hard drive faster than it can from a CD drive.

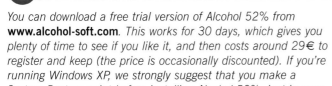

You can download a free trial version of Alcohol 52% from **www.alcohol-soft.com**. *This works for 30 days, which gives you plenty of time to see if you like it, and then costs around 29€ to register and keep (the price is occasionally discounted). If you're running Windows XP, we strongly suggest that you make a System Restore point before installing Alcohol 52%, just in case. The program will ask you to restart your system immediately after installation.*

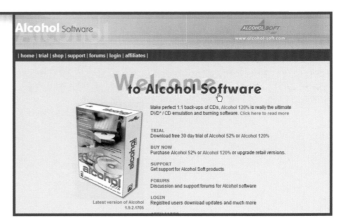

Alcohol 52% is a geeky program developed by geeks for geeks, but it's not so very difficult to use. Double-click the desktop shortcut to launch the program and have a look in the lower section of the split-pane interface. If your laptop currently has a CD drive connected, you will see two drives here: a physical drive, with its original drive letter (D in this case) and a new, virtual drive with a new drive letter (here it's E). This virtual drive is, of course, currently empty but it's ready to 'mount' disc images. What you need to do is make one.

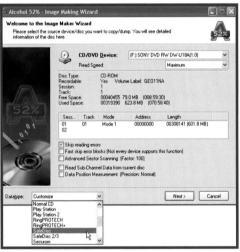

Pop any CD or DVD into the real drive. We're going to image a Microsoft Streets & Trips data disc, which means making a precise copy of the disc on the laptop's hard disk. Click the Image Making Wizard link.

Select your drive in the drop-down CD/DVD Device field. This tells Alcohol 52% to copy the disc that's in that drive. You should be able to leave all other settings at their default levels. However, if you're trying to copy a copy-protected disc, such as a computer game, you'll need to select the appropriate copy protection technology in the Datatype field. How do you know what copy-protection technology is there? The Alcohol 52% manual suggests an internet search and we echo this. Click Next to continue.

Alcohol 52% is ready to copy the disc and create an image file on your laptop's hard drive. Select a location and give the image file a meaningful name. You might want to choose or create a special folder specifically for your disc images. Leave the image format as the default MDS file type, and click Start.

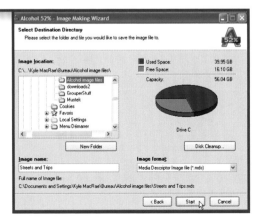

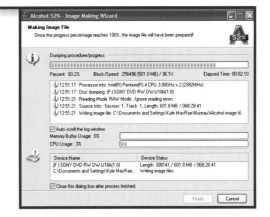

Alcohol 52% now copies the CD to the notebook's hard disk. This will take some time, depending on the speed of your drive. Don't worry about reported disk read errors, as there's nothing much you can do about them. The image file should play just fine regardless.

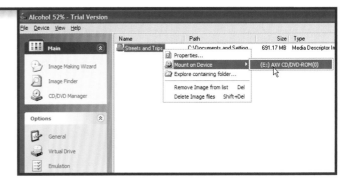

You can now remove the CD from the drive and, indeed, detach the drive from your notebook if it's possible to do so. All that remains is to mount the image in the virtual drive. Back in the main program, you should see your new image file listed in the upper pane. Right-click this, select Mount on Device and then select the virtual drive letter that you noted in Step 2.

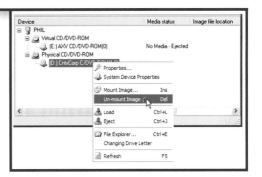

Once mounted, you can view, access and play the virtual disc in its virtual drive using My Computer. A virtual drive is, to Windows, the same as a real drive, just as a disc image is the same as the original disc. When you no longer need the disc, open Alcohol 52% again, right-click the virtual drive in the lower pane, and select Un-mount Image. The drive is now free and can be used to mount an alternative disc image.

Music and video

If you're thinking about using Alcohol to copy audio CDs and/or DVD movies in order to play music/watch films on your notebook, we suggest that you think again. On the music front, you're better off 'ripping' your CDs into the MP3, WMA or a similar compressed format instead and then playing tracks in a software music player. You'll save a great deal of disc space compared with imaging an audio CD and you don't need to bother with virtual drives at all.

If you want to take a movie on the road, the best option is to rip the original DVD into a highly-compressed but still high-quality movie file in the DivX or similar format. Again, this will save a tremendous amount of disk space – perhaps a 700MB file compared to 4GB or more – and disk space is always at a premium on a notebook.

However, the copyright implications of using a program like Alcohol 52% demand a cautionary word or two. Basically, if you copy any CD or DVD to which you do not own the copyright, you

are probably infringing the true copyright holder's rights. This is the case even when you make a personal backup copy of commercial material that you have paid for. It may seem fair enough to, say, make an image of a computer game so that you can play it on your notebook while you're on the road, but the legalities say otherwise (especially if you use software that circumvents, or 'cracks', copy-protection measures, as Alcohol 52% can do).

The reason why computer games require you to keep the disc in the drive while playing is to make piracy harder. For instance, if you lend a game to a mate, he can't simply install it on his own PC and play it forever after. True, you are unlikely to be prosecuted for copying your own games onto your own notebook for your own use, but you should only use software like this if you are aware of the issues. Proceed at your own risk, in short.

For more on entertainment on the move, see p.148–151.

Appendix 4 – Glossary

Here's an at-a-glance guide to some of the terms used throughout this manual. Let's start with a table of the storage units:

Name	Symbol	Size
Bit	b	A single binary unit (i.e. a 1 or a 0)
Byte	B	8 bits
Kilobit	Kb	1024 bits (= 128 bytes)
Kilobyte	KB	1024 bytes
Megabit	Mb	1,048,576 bits (= 131,072 bytes)
Megabyte	MB	1,048,576 bytes (= 1024 kilobytes)
Gigabyte	GB	1,073,741,824 bytes (= 1024 megabytes)

3G
Shorthand for third-generation telephone network, by which is meant a fast wireless network designed for transferring data to and from mobile devices.

ASF
Advanced Systems Format. A video and audio file format.

Bandwidth
A measure of how much data can be transferred at any one time. In terms of the internet and networking, greater bandwidth equates to higher speed.

Bluetooth
A short-range wireless networking technology.

Broadband
A general name for high-speed, always-on internet connections with bandwidth in the region of 500Kb/sec and up.

CF
CompactFlash. A memory card format.

Dial-up
A general name for internet connections conducted through a modem over a telephone line. A dial-up connection has a bandwidth of around 50Kb/sec.

DivX
A video compression technology.

EDGE
Enhanced Data Rates for GSM Evolution. One of the 3G network technologies.

Ethernet
A basic wired networking technology, where computers link up with cables in order to share files and services.

Expansion
Any method of adding to a device's native capability. For instance, you can increase storage space in a PDA by installing a memory card in its expansion slot.

FireWire (IEEE 1394)
A high-speed wired interface for connecting devices.

Flash ROM
Non-volatile, read-only memory (storage space) that contains a PDA's operating system.

GHz
Gigahertz. A measure of the speed of a computer processor. One GHz equals one billion clock cycles per second

Gmail
A free webmail service from Google (**www.gmail.com**)

GPRS
General Packet Radio Service. A technology used to send and receive data in discrete packets across a high-speed wireless network.

GPS
Global Positioning System. A satellite-based technology used to accurately deduce something's physical location anywhere on earth.

GSM
Global System for Mobile communications. The ubiquitous mobile telephone network, suited to phone calls and text messaging but not to internet access.

HTML
Hypertext Mark-up Language. A file format used in the creation of web pages.

IMAP4
Internet Message Access Protocol 4. A means of retrieving email messages from a remote server with an email program. Similar to POP3 but more flexible.

Instant messaging
Any technology that lets you send and receive text messages instantly through the internet.

IrDA
Infrared data exchange can be used to connect two compatible devices located at close quarters with a direct line of sight to one another.

ISP
Internet Service Provider. A company that provides access to the internet to subscribers.

Megapixel
One million pixels.

Memory card	A small, lightweight, durable storage medium used to transfer computer files and programs from one device to another and provide additional storage space. Ideally suited for use in PDAs.
MHz	Megahertz. A measure of the speed of a computer processor. One MHz equals one million clock cycles per second. Confusingly, MHz is also used in the context of GSM networks.
MMC	MultiMedia Card. A memory card format.
MMS	Multimedia Messaging System. A souped-up form of text messaging (SMS) which allows compatible mobile devices to send sound and video messages alongside text over a GSM (or faster) network.
Modem	A device that allows a computer or PDA to establish a dial-up connection with an ISP over an analogue telephone system.
MP3	MPEG-1 Audio Layer 3. An encoding and compression technology used to convert audio, especially music, into computer files.
MPEG	Moving Picture Experts Group. A series of standards used to encode video (MPEG-1, MPEG-2 and MPEG-4) and audio (MP3).
PC Card	Credit card-sized, plug-in expansion hardware that brings additional features to laptops (and some PDAs). For instance, you can upgrade a laptop to wireless networking capability with a Wi-Fi PC card.
PDF	Portable Document Format. A popular file format that preserves text and image layout.
Pixel	The smallest element of an image. In a computer or PDA display, it is a single point of light.
POP3	Post Office Protocol 3. The basic, universal standard for accessing email messages on a remote server.
QWERTY	The layout of keys on a (UK) English keyboard. The name refers to the position of the first six letters on the top row.
RAM	Random Access Memory. A volatile type of memory used to store data. You can increase the amount of RAM in a PDA by means of an expansion card.
RJ-11	A cable connection design commonly used with telephone systems.
RJ-45	A cable connection design commonly used with Ethernet computer networks.
SD	Secure Digital. A memory card format.
SDIO	Secure Digital Input/Output. An expansion slot interface on a PDA that allows peripheral devices, such as cameras and Bluetooth adapters, to be connected.

Server	A computer that supplies files, emails and services to another computer on demand.
SIM	Subscriber Identity Module. A small card used in GSM mobile phones. The card holds a microchip that stores information, including the phone's telephone number and a record of all calls and messages made and received. Without a SIM, a handset is useless.
SMS	Short Messaging Service. The technology that enables mobile phones to send and receive text messages of up to 160 characters over a GSM network.
S-video	An interface for transferring video output to another device, commonly used to connect a computer to a TV.
TFT	Thin Film Transistor. The technology used in the construction of liquid crystal displays, as used in computer monitors and PDAs.
UMTS	Universal Mobile Telecommunications System. The European standard for third-generation (3G) mobile telephone networks.
USB	Universal Serial Bus. A high-speed wired interface for connecting devices.
VGA	Video Graphics Array. A basic standard describing the resolution of computer-style displays. A VGA display measures 640 x 480 pixels.
VoIP	Voice over Internet Protocol. A technology that enables telephone calls to be made over the internet rather than through a normal telephone system.
WEP	Wired Equivalent Privacy. A means of encrypting a Wi-Fi network to prevent intrusion.
Wi-Fi	Wireless-Fidelity. The generic name for a family of wireless local networking technologies. There are three main Wi-Fi standards, known as 802.11a, b and g. The oldest of these, 802.11b, runs at a theoretical maximum speed of 11Mb/sec (about the same as the slowest version of Ethernet). This has since been largely replaced by 802.11g, which runs at 54Mb/sec. Hardware designed for either 802.11b or 802.11g will work together smoothly. 802.11a also runs at 54Mb/sec but is considerably less common and is not compatible with the other two standards.
WMV	Windows Media Video. A video compression technology.
WPA	Wi-Fi Protected Access. An alternative, stronger technology to WEP for encrypting and securing wireless networks.

Index

ACKNOWLEDGEMENTS

The author and publisher would like to thank the following for their help in the preparation of this manual:

Darika Ahrens	Steve Clark	Abigail Lovell
Barbara Bajkowski	Katherine Danby	Clare McMeel
Matt Ball	Gareth Davies	Anisa Topan
Joanna Boundy	Kate Hanson	Rianne de Voogt
Jim Buchanan	Jessica Hornblass	Paul Wardley
Mary Burt	Matt King	Adam Westley

Author	**Kyle MacRae**
Copy Editor	**Shena Deuchars**
Photography	**Iain McLean**
Page build	**James Robertson**
Index	**Nigel d'Auvergne**
Project Manager	**Louise McIntyre**